McDOUGAL LITTELL
The
AMERICANS
Reconstruction to the 21st Century

CURRICULUM

In-Depth Resources: Unit 2

Bridge to the 20th Century

McDougal Littell
A HOUGHTON MIFFLIN COMPANY
Evanston, Illinois • Boston • Dallas

Acknowledgments

CHAPTER 6

Excerpt from *The Birth and Babyhood of the Telephone*, published by American Telephone and Telegraph Company. Courtesy of AT&T Archives.

CHAPTER 7

Excerpt from *Call It Sleep* by Henry Roth. Copyright 1934, renewed 1962 by Henry Roth. Reprinted by permission of Farrar, Straus & Giroux, Inc.

CHAPTER 8

Excerpt from *Miracle at Kitty Hawk*, edited by Fred C. Kelly. Copyright 1951 by Fred C. Kelly. Reprinted by permission of Farrar, Straus & Giroux, Inc.

Excerpt from *Ragtime* by E. L. Doctorow. Copyright © 1974, 1975 by E. L. Doctorow. Reprinted by permission of Random House, Inc.

ISBN-13: 978-0-618-17607-6   ISBN-10: 0-618-17607-1

Printed in the United States of America.

9 10 11 12 – MDO – 08 07 06

CHAPTER 7 Immigrants and Urbanization, 1877–1914

CHAPTER 8 Life at the Turn of the Century, 1877–1917

Name _____ Date _____

GUIDED READING *Cultures Clash on the Prairie*

A. As you read about the conflicts that occurred during the settlement of the Western
frontier, answer questions about the time line below.

1858	Discovery of Gold in Colorado →	1. How did the discovery of gold affect the settlement of the West?
1864	Sand Creek Massacre →	2. What happened at Sand Creek?
1868	Treaty of Fort Laramie →	3. What were the terms of the Treaty of Fort Laramie? Why did it fail?
1874	Invasion by gold miners of the Sioux's sacred Black Hills	
1876	George A. Custer's Last Stand →	4. What happened at the Battle of Little Bighorn?
1887	The policy of assimilation formalized in the Dawes Act →	5. What was the purpose of the Dawes Act?
1890	The Spread of the Ghost Dance movement; the death of Sitting Bull; the Battle of Wounded Knee →	6. What happened at Wounded Knee Creek?

B. On the back of this paper, identify **Sitting Bull** and describe how he tried to deal
with the problems his people faced.

Name _____ Date _____

GUIDED READING *Settling the Great Plains*

A. As you read this section, note how each of the factors listed below (Causes) helped to settle the West and turned the eastern Great Plains into the nation's "breadbasket" (Effects).

Causes	Effects
1. Land grants given to the railroads	
2. The Homestead Act and related laws passed in the 1870s	
3. Inventions and improvements in farm technology	
4. The Morrill Land Grant Acts and Hatch Act	

B. What were some hardships faced by frontier farmers? (Note: one hardship per box)

C. On the back of this paper, explain **homesteader, soddy,** and **bonanza farm.**

Name _____ Date _____

CHAPTER
5
Section 3

GUIDED READING *Farmers and the Populist Movement*

A. As you read this section, take notes to answer questions about the pressures that made farming increasingly unprofitable.

In the late 1800s, farmers faced increasing costs and decreasing crop prices.

1. Why had farming become unprofitable during this period?	2. Why did farmers support bimetallism or "free silver"?

In 1892, farmers and farm organizations, such as the Grange, found support in Populism and the People's Party.

3. What economic reforms did the People's Party call for?	4. What political reforms did the party call for?

In 1896, the Populists supported presidential candidate William Jennings Bryan.

5. What factions did Bryan and the Populists see as opposing forces in the presidential election of 1896?	6. In what ways did the results of the 1896 election confirm this view?

B. On the back of this paper, note who **Mary Elizabeth Lease** and **Oliver Hudson Kelley** were. Then, briefly explain the relationship between **inflation/deflation** and the **"Cross of Gold"** speech.

Name _____ Date _____

BUILDING VOCABULARY *Changes on the Western Frontier*

A. Matching Match the definition in the second column with the term or name in the first column. Write the appropriate letter next to the word.

_____ 1. Oliver Hudson Kelley   a. African-American migrants to Kansas

_____ 2. Chisholm Trail   b. grassland extending through the West

_____ 3. Populism   c. tried to "Americanize" Native Americans

_____ 4. exodusters   d. offered free western land to settlers

_____ 5. Great Plains   e. started the Grange

_____ 6. gold standard   f. movement of the people

_____ 7. Homestead Act   g. backing dollars solely with gold

_____ 8. Dawes Act   h. major cattle route from Texas to Kansas

B. Evaluating Write *T* in the blank if the statement is true. If the statement is false, write *F* in the blank and then write the corrected statement on the line below.

_____ 1. Bimetallism is a monetary system based solely on silver.

_____

_____ 2. William McKinley was the Republican candidate in the 1896 presidential election— and its eventual winner.

_____

_____ 3. The Morrill Act gave federal land to the states to help finance railroad construction.

_____

_____ 4. The Battle of Wounded Knee brought the Indian wars to an end.

_____

_____ 5. Sitting Bull, leader of the Apache, resisted western settlement by whites.

_____

Name _____   Date _____

SKILLBUILDER PRACTICE *Creating Written Presentations*

Choose a topic from Section 1 that interests you and prepare the blueprint for a written presentation on that topic. Use the boxes below to describe the topic you wish to research as well as the hypothesis you have formulated based on your research. Then create an outline for your written presentation using the template provided. (See Skillbuilder Handbook, pp. R34–R35.)

Topic

Hypothesis

Outline

I. _____

   A. _____

   B. _____

   C. _____

II. _____

   A. _____

   B. _____

   C. _____

CHAPTER

5

Section 2

SKILLBUILDER PRACTICE *Creating Models*

Models are visual representations of geographical areas, villages, cities, inventions, buildings, and other physical objects of historical importance. Models, which can be either two-dimensional or three-dimensional representations, provide scholars with a highly-detailed example of the way people lived during particular aspects of history.

Read the text under the subheading "Dugouts and Soddies" on pages 216–217 and study the photograph on page 216. Then create a model of a soddy in the space provided below. You may do further research on the soddy in order to enhance your model. (See Skillbuilder Handbook, page R31.)

CHAPTER 5

Section 1

RETEACHING ACTIVITY *Cultures Clash on the Prairie*

Reading Comprehension Choose the best answer. Write your answer in the blank.

_____ 1. The _____ provided many basic needs for the Plains Indians and was central to their way of life.
    a. horse
    b. buffalo
    c. dog
    d. wolf

_____ 2. The prospect of striking _____ drew many settlers to the Great Plains.
    a. gold
    b. oil
    c. tin
    d. copper

_____ 3. In the Treaty of Fort Laramie, the _____ agreed to move to a reservation.
    a. Navajo
    b. Sioux
    c. Cherokee
    d. Seminole

_____ 4. The American cowboy drew many of his customs from ranchers in _____.
    a. Spain
    b. Canada
    c. Mexico
    d. Cuba

_____ 5. The demand for _____ in cities led to the growth of the cattle industry.
    a. bones
    b. leather
    c. poultry
    d. beef

_____ 6. About twenty-five percent of all cowboys were _____.
    a. Asian
    b. Native American
    c. African American
    d. Mexican

_____ 7. General George Custer and his troops were routed at the _____.
    a. Battle of Little Big Horn
    b. Battle of Wounded Knee
    c. Massacre at Sand Creek
    d. Battle of Fallen Timbers

_____ 8. _____ was NOT a factor in ending the open range era.
    a. Overgrazing of land
    b. Rise of the railroads
    c. Extended bad weather
    d. The invention of barbed wire

Name _____   Date _____

CHAPTER
5
Section 2

RETEACHING ACTIVITY *Settling the Great Plains*

Evaluating

A. Write *T* in the blank if the statement is true. If the statement is false, write *F* in the blank and then write the corrected statement on the line below.

_____ 1. The completion of a transcontinental railroad helped to make rapid settlement of the West possible.

_____

_____ 2. In 1889, settlers claimed some 2 million acres in less than a day in a free land giveaway in what is now Minnesota.

_____

_____ 3. Women played little role in settling the West.

_____

_____ 4. The windmill prevented crop dehydration by bringing up underground water.

_____

_____ 5. With forestland abundant on the Plains, most settlers built their homes out of wood.

_____

Finding Main Ideas

B. Choose the word that most accurately completes the sentences below.

Yellowstone National Park	Nebraska	Cyrus McCormick
California	Utah	barbed wire
John Deere	immigrants	African Americans

1. _____ prevented animals from trampling crops and wandering off.

2. In 1872, the federal government created _____ in an effort to help conserve the frontier.

3. By 1880, many settlers in Minnesota and Wisconsin were _____.

4. _____ invented the steel plow in 1837.

5. Two railroad lines met in _____ to form the first transcontinental railroad.

CHAPTER

5

Section 3

RETEACHING ACTIVITY *Farmers and the Populist Movement*

Finding Main Ideas

The following questions deal with events of the Jeffersonian Era. Answer them in the space provided.

1. What problems did many Plains farmers face during the late 1800s?

_____

_____

2. What was the Grange's plan for improving conditions for farmers?

_____

_____

3. What did the Populist Party platform call for?

_____

_____

4. What were the consequences of the Panic of 1893?

_____

_____

5. What was the difference between the "gold bugs" and the "silverites"?

_____

_____

6. How did the presidential election of 1896 bring an end to populism?

_____

_____

GEOGRAPHY APPLICATION: REGION

Land Regions of the West

Section 2

Directions: Read the paragraphs below and study the map carefully. Then answer the questions that follow.

The western United States contains many land regions. Plains are broad, level lands. Plateaus, also level, are elevated and often drier lands. Basins are fairly low-lying areas. The landforms typical of ranges are long rows of mountains. Lowlands are areas lower than neighboring areas. Valleys are narrow lowlands between mountains.

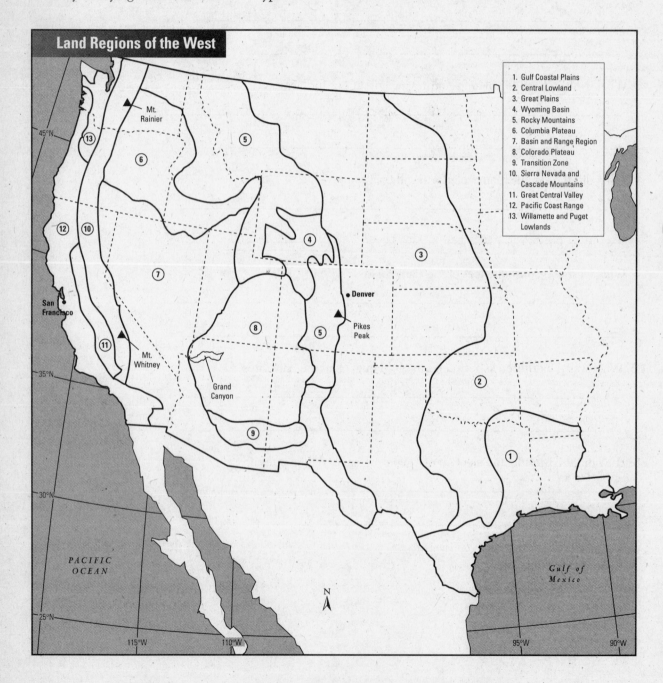

Land Regions of the West

1. Gulf Coastal Plains
2. Central Lowland
3. Great Plains
4. Wyoming Basin
5. Rocky Mountains
6. Columbia Plateau
7. Basin and Range Region
8. Colorado Plateau
9. Transition Zone
10. Sierra Nevada and Cascade Mountains
11. Great Central Valley
12. Pacific Coast Range
13. Willamette and Puget Lowlands

Interpreting Text and Visuals

1. Which single type of landform is found in regions 5, 7, 10, and 12? _____

2. What regions extend all the way from Canada to Texas? _____
   _____

3. Which land regions would you cross if you traveled due west from Denver
   to San Francisco?

   _____

   _____

4. In which land region is each of the following physical features located?

   a. Pikes Peak _____

   b. Mt. Rainier _____

   c. Grand Canyon _____

   d. Mt. Whitney _____

5. Which is the only region separated into two sections? _____

6. Approximately which line of longitude forms the dividing line between the Great
   Plains and the Rocky Mountains—95°W, 100°W, 105°W, or 110°W? _____

7. What is the main difference between the land bordering the Gulf of Mexico and
   the land bordering the Pacific Ocean? _____

   _____

   _____

8. The Wyoming Basin is basically an extension of the Great Plains. Look at the map
   again. Why do you think the Wyoming Basin played a major role
   in the settling of the Far West?

   _____

   _____

   _____

CHAPTER 5

Section 1

PRIMARY SOURCE The Battle of the Little Bighorn

Two Moon, a Cheyenne warrior, fought against General Custer and the Seventh Cavalry in the Battle of the Little Bighorn on June 25, 1876. What is your impression of the battle after reading this excerpt from Two Moon's eyewitness account?

The Sioux rode up the ridge on all sides, riding very fast. The Cheyennes went up the left way. Then the shooting was quick, quick. Pop—pop—pop very fast. Some of the soldiers were down on their knees, some standing. Officers all in front. The smoke was like a great cloud, and everywhere the Sioux went the dust rose like smoke. We circled all round him—swirling like water round a stone. We shoot, we ride fast, we shoot again. Soldiers drop, and horses fall on them. Soldiers in line drop, but one man rides up and down the line—all the time shouting. He rode a sorrel horse with white face and white fore-legs. I don't know who he was. He was a brave man.

Indians keep swirling round and round, and the soldiers killed only a few. Many soldiers fell. At last all horses killed but five. Once in a while some man would break out and run toward the river, but he would fall. At last about a hundred men and five horsemen stood on the hill all bunched together. All along the bugler kept blowing his commands. He was very brave too. Then a chief was killed. I hear it was Long Hair [Custer], I don't know; and then the five horsemen and the bunch of men, maybe forty, started toward the river. The man on the sorrel horse led them, shouting all the time. He wore a buckskin shirt, and had long black hair and mustache. He fought hard with a big knife. His men were all covered with white dust. I couldn't tell whether they were officers or not. One man all alone ran far down toward the river, then round up over the hill. I thought he was going to escape, but a Sioux fired and hit him in the head. He was the last man. He wore braid on his arms [signifying a sergeant].

All the soldiers were now killed, and the bodies were stripped. After that no one could tell which were officers. The bodies were left where they fell. We had no dance that night. We were sorrowful.

Next day four Sioux chiefs and two Cheyennes and I, Two Moon, went upon the battlefield to count the dead. One man carried a little bundle of sticks. When we came to dead men, we took a little stick and gave it to another man, so we counted the dead. There were 388. There were thirty-nine Sioux and seven Cheyennes killed, and about a hundred wounded.

Some white soldiers were cut with knives, to make sure they were dead; and the war women had mangled some. Most of them were left just where they fell. We came to the man with the big mustache; he lay down the hills towards the river. The Indians did not take his buckskin shirt. The Sioux said, "That is a big chief. That is Long Hair." I don't know. I had never seen him. The man on the white-faced horse was the bravest man.

That day as the sun was getting low our young men came up the Little Horn riding hard. Many white soldiers were coming in a big boat, and when we looked we could see the smoke rising. I called my people together, and we hurried up to the Little Horn, into Rotten Grass Valley. We camped there three days, and then rode swiftly back over our old trail to the east. Sitting Bull went back into the Rosebud and down the Yellowstone, and away to the north. I did not see him again.

from Hamlin Garland, "General Custer's Last Fight as Seen by Two Moon," *McClure's Magazine*, Vol. 11, 1898, 443–448. Reprinted in Wayne Moquin, ed, *Great Documents in American Indian History* (New York: Praeger Publishers, 1973), 226–229.

Activity Options

1. Work with a group of classmates to prepare a script about the Battle of Little Bighorn for a segment of a TV documentary entitled The Plains Wars.
2. Refer to pages 203–206 in your textbook. Then make a cause-and-effect diagram to illustrate the causes and effects of the Battle of Little Bighorn. Share your diagram with your classmates.
3. Design a historical plaque or monument that might be placed at the battle site where this bloody clash took place. Make a sketch or a three-dimensional model and share it with your classmates.

CHAPTER 5

Section 2

PRIMARY SOURCE Letter from a Woman Homesteader

In 1909 Elinore Rupert left Denver, Colorado, with her daughter Jerrine and went to Wyoming to work as a housekeeper for Clyde Stewart, a rancher whom she later married. This is a letter she wrote to her former employer.

November, 1913.

Dear Mrs. Coney,—

This is Sunday and I suppose I ought not to be writing, but I must write to you and I may not have another chance soon. Both your letters have reached me, and now that our questions are settled we can proceed to proceed.

Now, this is the letter I have been wanting to write you for a long time, but could not because until now I had not actually proven all I wanted to prove. Perhaps it will not interest you, but if you see a woman who wants to homestead and is a little afraid she will starve, you can tell her what I am telling you.

I never did like to theorize, and so this year I set out to prove that a woman could ranch if she wanted to. We like to grow potatoes on new ground, that is, newly cleared land on which no crop has been grown. Few weeds grow on new land, so it makes less work. So I selected my potato-patch, and the man ploughed it, although I could have done that if Clyde would have let me. I cut the potatoes, Jerrine helped, and we dropped them in the rows. The man covered them, that ends the man's part. By that time the garden ground was ready, so I planted the garden. I had almost an acre in vegetables. I irrigated and I cultivated it myself.

We had all the vegetables we could possibly use, and now Jerrine and I have put in our cellar full, and this is what we have: one large bin of potatoes (more than two tons), half a ton of carrots, a large bin of beets, one of turnips, one of onions, one of parsnips, and on the other side of the cellar we have more than one hundred heads of cabbage. I have experimented and found a kind of squash that can be raised here, and that the ripe ones keep well and make good pies; also that the tender ones make splendid pickles, quite equal to cucumbers. I was glad to stumble on to that, because pickles are hard to manufacture when you have nothing to work with. Now I have plenty. They told me when I came that I could not even raise common beans,

but I tried and succeeded. And also I raised lots of green tomatoes, and, as we like them preserved, I made them all up that way. Experimenting along another line, I found that I could make catchup, as delicious as that of tomatoes, of gooseberries. I made it exactly the same as I do the tomatoes and I am delighted. Gooseberries were very fine and very plentiful this year, so I put up a great many. I milked ten cows twice a day all summer; have sold enough butter to pay for a year's supply of flour and gasoline. We use a gasoline lamp. I have raised enough chickens to completely renew my flock, and all we wanted to eat, and have some fryers to go into the winter with. I have enough turkeys for all of our birthdays and holidays.

I raised a great many flowers and I worked several days in the field. In all I have told about I have had no help but Jerrine. Clyde's mother spends each summer with us, and she helped me with the cooking and the babies. Many of my neighbors did better than I did, although I know many town people would doubt my doing so much, but I did it. I have tried every kind of work this ranch affords, and I can do any of it. Of course I *am* extra strong, but those who try know that strength and knowledge come with doing. I just love to experiment, to work, and to prove out things, so that ranch life and "roughing it" just suit me.

from Elinore Stewart, *Letters of a Woman Homesteader* (Lincoln: University of Nebraska Press, 1961), 279–282.

Discussion Questions

1. According to her letter, what did Elinore Rupert Stewart finally prove?
2. How would you describe her attitude toward being a homesteader?
3. Do you think Stewart's letter creates a fair portrait of what life was like for women homesteaders? Why or why not? Cite evidence from your textbook to support your opinion.

CHAPTER 5

Section 3

PRIMARY SOURCE *from* William Jennings Bryan's "Cross of Gold" Speech

During the 1896 Democratic convention, politicians fiercely debated whether to support the gold standard or bimetallism. William Jennings Bryan, the final speaker at the convention, delivered an eloquent appeal for unlimited coinage of silver. As you read this excerpt from his famous speech, consider his arguments.

I would be presumptuous, indeed, to present myself against the distinguished gentlemen to whom you have listened if this were but a measuring of ability; but this is not a contest among persons. The humblest citizen in all the land when clad in armor of a righteous cause is stronger than all the whole hosts of error that they can bring. I come to speak to you in defense of a cause as holy as the cause of liberty—the cause of humanity. . . .

Here is the line of battle. We care not upon which issue they force the fight. We are prepared to meet them on either issue or on both. If they tell us that the gold standard is the standard of civilization, we reply to them that this, the most enlightened of all nations of the earth, has never declared for a gold standard, and both the parties this year are declaring against it. If the gold standard is the standard of civilization, why, my friends, should we not have it? So if they come to meet us on that, we can present the history of our nation. More than that, we can tell them this, that they will search the pages of history in vain to find a single instance in which the common people of any land ever declared themselves in favor of a gold standard. They can find where the holders of fixed investments have.

Mr. Carlisle said in 1878 that this was a struggle between the idle holders of idle capital and the struggling masses who produce the wealth and pay the taxes of the country; and my friends, it is simply a question that we shall decide upon which side shall the Democratic Party fight. Upon the side of the idle holders of idle capital, or upon the side of the struggling masses? That is the question that the party must answer first; and then it must be answered by each individual hereafter. The sympathies of the Democratic Party, as described by the platform, are on the side of the struggling masses, who have ever been the foundation of the Democratic Party.

There are two ideas of government. There are those who believe that if you just legislate to make the well-to-do prosperous that their prosperity will leak through on those below. The Democratic idea has been that if you legislate to make the masses prosperous their prosperity will find its way up and through every class that rests upon it.

You come to us and tell us that the great cities are in favor of the gold standard. I tell you that the great cities rest upon these broad and fertile prairies. Burn down your cities and leave our farms, and your cities will spring up again as if by magic. But destroy our farms and the grass will grow in the streets of every city in this country. . . .

If they dare to come out and in the open defend the gold standard as a good thing, we shall fight them to the uttermost, having behind us the producing masses of the nation and the world. Having behind us the commercial interests and the laboring interests and all the toiling masses, we shall answer their demands for a gold standard by saying to them, you shall not press down upon the brow of labor this crown of thorns. You shall not crucify mankind upon a cross of gold.

from Encyclopaedia Britannica, 1895–1904: *Populism, Imperialism, and Reform,* vol. 12 of *The Annals of America* (Chicago: Encyclopaedia Britannica, 1968), 100–105.

Activity Options

1. Deliver Bryan's "Cross of Gold" speech to your classmates. Then discuss why you think this speech moved the Democratic Party to nominate Bryan as its candidate for president.
2. During the 1896 presidential election, the debate over the gold standard raged. The Republican Party favored it, while the Democratic Party supported bimetallism. Create a campaign button that might have been used by either party.
3. Imagine that it is 1896. With your classmates, hold a mock debate in which you role-play a free silverite or a gold bug. If you argue against the gold standard, use Bryan's arguments to support your position. (Review pages 222–223 in your textbook.)

CHAPTER **5**

Section 2

LITERATURE SELECTION *from* **My Ántonia**
by Willa Cather

Both Willa Cather and Jim Burden, the narrator of My Ántonia, *left Virginia and settled on a farm in Nebraska. As you read this excerpt from Cather's novel, think about how Jim as a boy first reacts to life on the plains.*

Early the next morning I ran out-of-doors to look about me. I had been told that ours was the only wooden house west of Black Hawk—until you came to the Norwegian settlement, where there were several. Our neighbours lived in sod houses and dugouts—comfortable, but not very roomy. Our white frame house, with a storey and half-storey above the basement, stood at the east end of what I might call the farmyard, with the windmill close by the kitchen door. From the windmill the ground sloped westward, down to the barns and granaries and pig-yards. This slope was trampled hard and bare, and washed out in winding gullies by the rain. Beyond the corncribs, at the bottom of the shallow draw [gully], was a muddy little pond, with rusty willow bushes growing about it. The road from the post-office came directly by our door, crossed the farmyard, and curved round this little pond, beyond which it began to climb the gentle swell of unbroken prairie to the west. There, along the western sky-line it skirted a great cornfield, much larger than any field I had ever seen. This cornfield, and the sorghum patch behind the barn, were the only broken land in sight. Everywhere, as far as the eye could reach, there was nothing but rough, shaggy, red grass, most of it as tall as I.

North of the house, inside the ploughed fire-breaks, grew a thick-set strip of box-elder trees, low and bushy, their leaves already turning yellow. This hedge was nearly a quarter of a mile long, but I had to look very hard to see it at all. The little trees were insignificant against the grass. It seemed as if the grass were about to run over them, and over the plum-patch behind the sod chicken-house.

As I looked about me I felt that the grass was the country, as the water is the sea. The red of the grass made all the great prairie the colour of wine-stains, or of certain seaweeds when they are first washed up. And there was so much motion in it; the

As I looked about me I felt that the grass was the country, as the water is the sea.

whole country seemed, somehow, to be running.

I had almost forgotten that I had a grandmother, when she came out, her sunbonnet on her head, a grain-sack in her hand, and asked me if I did not want to go to the garden with her to dig potatoes for dinner.

The garden, curiously enough, was a quarter of a mile from the house, and the way to it led up a shallow draw past the cattle corral. Grandmother called my attention to a stout hickory cane, tipped with copper, which hung by a leather thong from her belt. This, she said, was her rattlesnake cane. I must never go to the garden without a heavy stick or a corn-knife; she had killed a good many rattlers on her way back and forth. A little girl who lived on the Black Hawk road was bitten on the ankle and had been sick all summer.

I can remember exactly how the country looked to me as I walked beside my grandmother along the faint wagon-tracks on that early September morning. Perhaps the glide of long railway travel was still with me, for more than anything else I felt motion in the landscape; in the fresh, easy-blowing morning wind, and in the earth itself, as if the shaggy grass were a sort of loose hide, and underneath it herds of wild buffalo were galloping, galloping . . .

Alone, I should never have found the garden—except, perhaps, for the big yellow pumpkins that lay about unprotected by their withering vines—and I felt very little interest in it when I got there. I wanted to walk straight on through the red grass and over the edge of the world, which could not be very far away. The light air about me told me that the world ended here: only the ground and sun and sky were left, and if one went a little farther there would be only sun and sky, and one would float off into them, like the tawny hawks which sailed over our heads making slow shadows on the grass. While grandmother took the pitchfork we found standing in one of the rows and dug potatoes, while I picked them up out of the soft brown earth and put them into the bag, I kept looking up at the hawks that were doing what I might so easily do.

When grandmother was ready to go, I said I would like to stay up there in the garden awhile.

She peered down at me from under her sun-bonnet. "Aren't you afraid of snakes?"

"A little," I admitted, "but I'd like to stay, anyhow."

"Well, if you see one, don't have anything to do with him. The big yellow and brown ones won't hurt you; they're bull-snakes and help to keep the gophers down. Don't be scared if you see anything look out of that hole in the bank over there. That's a badger hole. He's about as big as a big 'possum, and his face is striped, black and white. He takes a chicken once in a while, but I won't let the men harm him. In a new country a body feels friendly to the animals. I like to have him come out and watch me when I'm at work."

Grandmother swung the bag of potatoes over her shoulder and went down the path, leaning forward a little. The road followed the windings of the draw; when she came to the first bend, she waved at me and disappeared. I was left alone with this new feeling of lightness and content.

I sat down in the middle of the garden, where snakes could scarcely approach unseen, and leaned my back against a warm yellow pumpkin. There were some ground-cherry bushes growing along the furrows, full of fruit. I turned back the papery tri-angular sheaths that protected the berries and ate a few. All about me giant grasshoppers, twice as big as any I had ever seen, were doing acrobatic feats among the dried vines. The gophers scurried up and down the ploughed ground. There in the shel-tered draw-bottom the wind did not blow very hard, but I could hear it singing its humming tune up on the level, and I could see the tall grasses wave. The earth was warm under me, and warm as I crumbled it through my fingers. Queer little red bugs came out and moved in slow squadrons around me. Their backs were polished vermilion, with black spots. I kept as still as I could. Nothing happened. I did not expect anything to happen. I was something that lay under the sun and felt it, like the pumpkins, and I did not want to be any-

I sat down in the middle of the garden, where snakes could scarcely approach unseen.

thing more. I was entirely happy. Perhaps we feel like that when we die and become a part of some-thing entire, whether it is sun and air, or goodness and knowledge. At any rate, that is happiness; to be dissolved into something complete and great. When it comes to one, it comes as naturally as sleep.

On Sunday morning Otto Fuchs was to drive us over to make the acquaintance of our new Bohemian neighbours. We were taking them some provisions, as they had come to live on a wild place where there was no garden or chicken-house, and very little broken land. Fuchs brought up a sack of potatoes and a piece of cured pork from the cellar, and grandmother packed some loaves of Saturday's bread, a jar of butter, and several pumpkin pies in the straw of the wagon-box. We clambered up to the front seat and jolted off past the little pond and along the road that climbed to the big cornfield.

I could hardly wait to see what lay beyond that cornfield; but there was only red grass like ours, and nothing else, though from the high wagon-seat one could look off a long way. The road ran about like a wild thing, avoiding the deep draws, crossing them where they were wide and shallow. And all along it, wherever it looped or ran, the sunflowers grew; some of them were as big as little trees, with great rough leaves and many branches which bore dozens of blossoms. They made a gold ribbon across the prairie. Occasionally one of the horses would tear off with his teeth a plant full of blossoms, and walk along munching it, the flowers nodding in time to his bites as he ate down toward them.

The Bohemian family, grandmother told me as we drove along, had bought the homestead of a fel-low countryman, Peter Krajiek, and had paid him more than it was worth. Their agreement with him was made before they left the old country, through a cousin of his, who was also a relative of Mrs. Shimerda. The Shimerdas were the first Bohemian family to come to this part of the county. Krajiek was their only interpreter, and could tell them any-thing he chose. They could not speak enough English to ask for advice, or even to make their most pressing wants known. One son, Fuchs said, was well-grown, and strong enough to work the land; but the father was old and frail and knew nothing about farming. He was a weaver by trade;

had been a skilled workman on tapestries and upholstery materials. He had brought his fiddle with him, which wouldn't be of much use here, though he used to pick up money by it at home.

"If they're nice people, I hate to think of them spending the winter in that cave of Krajiek's," said grandmother. "It's no better than a badger hole; no proper dugout at all. And I hear he's made them pay twenty dollars for his old cookstove that ain't worth ten."

"Yes'm," said Otto; "and he's sold 'em his oxen and his two bony old horses for the price of good work-teams. I'd have interfered about the horses— the old man can understand some German—if I'd 'a' thought it would do any good. But Bohemians has a natural distrust of Austrians."

Grandmother looked interested. "Now, why is that, Otto?"

Fuchs wrinkled his brow and nose. "Well, ma'm, it's politics. It would take me a long while to explain."

The land was growing rougher; I was told that we were approaching Squaw Creek, which cut up the west half of the Shimerdas' place and made the land of little value for farming. Soon we could see the broken, grassy clay cliffs which indicated the windings of the stream, and the glittering tops of the cottonwoods and ash trees that grew down in the ravine. Some of the cottonwoods had already turned, and the yellow leaves and shining white bark made them look like the gold and silver trees in fairy tales.

As we approached the Shimerdas' dwelling, I could still see nothing but rough red hillocks, and draws with shelving banks and long roots hanging out where the earth had crumbled away. Presently, against one of those banks, I saw a sort of shed, thatched with the same wine-coloured grass that grew everywhere. Near it tilted a shattered windmill frame, that had no wheel. We drove up to this skeleton to tie our horses, and then I saw a door and window sunk deep in the draw-bank. The door stood open, and a woman and a girl of fourteen ran out and looked up at us hopefully. A little girl trailed along behind them. The woman had on her head the same embroidered shawl with silk fringes that she wore when she had alighted from the train at Black Hawk. She was not old, but she was certainly not young. Her face was alert and lively, with a sharp chin and shrewd little eyes. She shook

grandmother's hand energetically.

"Very glad, very glad!" she ejaculated. Immediately she pointed to the bank out of which she had emerged and said, "House no good, house no good!"

Grandmother nodded consolingly. "You'll get fixed up comfortable after while, Mrs. Shimerda; make good house."

My grandmother always spoke in a very loud tone to foreigners, as if they were deaf. She made Mrs. Shimerda understand the friendly intention of our visit, and the Bohemian woman handled the loaves of bread and even smelled them, and examined the pies with lively curiosity, exclaiming, "Much good, much thank!" —and again she wrung grandmother's hand.

The oldest son, Ambroz—they called it Ambrosch—came out of the cave and stood beside his mother. He was nineteen years old, short and broad-backed, with a close-cropped, flat head, and a wide, flat face. His hazel eyes were little and shrewd, like his mother's, but more sly and suspicious; they fairly snapped at the food. The family had been living on corn-cakes and sorghum molasses for three days.

The family had been living on corn-cakes and sorghum molasses for three days.

The little girl was pretty, but Án-tonia—they accented the name thus, strongly, when they spoke to her—was still prettier. I remembered what the conductor had said about her eyes. They were big and warm and full of light, like the sun shining on brown pools in the wood. Her skin was brown, too, and in her cheeks she had a glow of rich, dark colour. Her brown hair was curly and wild-looking. The little sister, whom they called Yulka (Julka), was fair, and seemed mild and obedient. While I stood awkwardly confronting the two girls, Krajiek came up from the barn to see what was going on.

Research Options

1. Find out more about the plants and animals of the prairie. Then work with classmates to make a bulletin board display, including pictures and captions.
2. Find out more about dugouts and soddies that settlers like the Shimerdas lived in. Then make a set of interior and exterior sketches to show what a typical settler's home looked like. Display your sketches in the classroom.

CHAPTER 5

Section 1

AMERICAN LIVES Chief Joseph
Spokesman for His People

"The old men are all dead. [My brother] who led the young men is dead. It is cold, and we have no blankets. The little children are freezing to death. . . . From where the sun now stands, I will fight no more forever."—Chief Joseph, speech when surrendering to the U.S. Army, October 5, 1877

Chief Joseph (c. 1840–1904), a leader of the Nez Perce [něz' pûrs'] tribe, wanted to preserve his people's homeland. When white pressure for the land became too strong, he tried to lead his people to safety. Both efforts, however, failed.

The Nez Perce lived in peace near the Oregon/Washington border. By the 1860s, though, settlers wanted their rich land. Some Nez Perce bands gave up their land, but a chief named Old Joseph refused to yield the fertile Wallowa Valley. In 1871, he died and his two sons took control of the band. The older son, also Joseph, had the Native American name Hin-mah-too-yah-lat-kekht ("thunder coming from water over land") and held civil but not military authority.

When white settlers moved into the Wallowa Valley, Joseph protested to the government. President Ulysses S. Grant ruled that the valley was part of a reservation that belonged to the Nez Perce. Whites refused to leave, however, and two years later a new presidential order reversed the previous one. Joseph appealed to the government again. He impressed General Oliver Howard and others with his eloquent defense of his people's claim to their land. But they ruled against him. Howard ordered Joseph and his people to leave—in 30 days. Joseph calmed tempers and moved his people. Then, while camped near the reservation, angry younger warriors attacked and killed 20 settlers.

Thinking that war was now inevitable, Joseph agreed to join the warriors. This began a 1,700-mile journey that lasted many months and was marked by several Nez Perce victories over the pursuing army. Newspapers reported incorrectly that Joseph was the military leader and main strategist. He did take part in discussions among chiefs, and he led the defenses of the Nez Perce camps. However, he mainly represented the tribe in meetings with army officers. Thus, his name—Chief Joseph—entered news accounts.

The Nez Perce band, several hundred strong, moved eastward. After defeating the army at White Bird Canyon in Idaho, they were joined by another band that had left the reservation after an unprovoked attack by the army. They gained fighters—and also gained more women and children. They beat back the pursuing Howard at the Clearwater River and then moved into Montana. After a costly victory along the Big Hole River in Montana, they turned south.

The Nez Perce had hoped to make an alliance with the Crow but were unable to reach an agreement. The chiefs decided to head for Canada, hoping to join with Sitting Bull and his Sioux. They had to cross Montana from south to north, but supplies were running low and the cold coming in. They repelled another army attack at Canyon Creek and raced north. Howard had telegraphed for army units throughout the area to join the chase. Finally, just 30 miles south of the Canadian border, they were trapped by an overwhelming force of soldiers. The Nez Perce caused heavy casualties but suffered high losses of their own. When Howard and reinforcements arrived, Joseph and the remaining Nez Perce surrendered.

Many of the Nez Perce died when they were moved to the Indian Territory. But their long trek had roused popular sympathy, which persuaded the government to allow them to resettle in the Northwest. Joseph lived almost 30 more years but he never again lived in the Wallowa Valley.

Questions

1. What caused the Nez Perce war?
2. Would you describe Joseph's role as primarily political or military? Include details to support your view.
3. What aspects of the flight of Chief Joseph and his band do you think aroused popular sympathy and why?

CHAPTER 5

Section 3

AMERICAN LIVES Mary Elizabeth Lease

Taking a Stand for Farmers' Rights

"We meet in the midst of a nation brought to the verge of moral, political, and material ruin. Corruption dominates the ballot-box . . . [and] the Congress. . . . The fruits of the toil of millions are boldly stolen to build up colossal fortunes for a few . . . and the possessors of these, in turn, despise the Republic and endanger liberty."—Populist party platform (1892)

Mary Elizabeth Lease had a long career urging reform causes. She gained fame, though, for her passionate speeches on behalf of farmers and the Populist party in the 1890s.

Lease (1853–1933) was born in western Pennsylvania to Irish immigrants. She moved to Kansas at age 17 to teach, where she met her husband, Charles Lease, a pharmacist. They tried farming in Kansas and then in Texas but returned to Kansas and the pharmacy business in 1883. She began to address meetings to raise money for a group called the Irish National League. She soon expanded her interests to include the Farmers Alliance and the Knights of Labor. By 1890, her career as a speaker was flourishing.

Lease was a passionate speaker, willing to stretch the truth for effect. When she spoke for the Irish National League, for instance, she sometimes said that she had been born in Ireland. Her speeches were built on emotion, not logic, and with them she roused the crowd. She became so carried away that sometimes she could not remember what she had said. Supporters called her "our Queen Mary." Enemies referred to her as "the Kansas Pythoness." She sometimes used the name Mary Ellen, which was transformed by foes into "Mary Yellin."

Her speaking career began in Kansas, where she delivered more than 160 speeches in 1890 alone. Soon she was campaigning in the West and the South. In early 1892, Lease became one of those who plotted a strategy to make the Populist party a national force. Her strength was speaking, however. At the Populist convention of July 1892, she gave the speech that seconded the nomination of James Weaver of Iowa for president. She campaigned with Weaver across the midwest and South, stirring crowds with her cry that farmers should "raise less corn and more hell." She complained that the wealthy had taken control of the country. "It is no longer a government of the people, by the people, and for the people," she said, "but a government of Wall Street, by Wall Street, and for Wall Street." She said that it was time for women to enter politics: "Thank God we women are blameless for this political muddle you men have dragged us into. . . . Ours is a grand and holy mission . . . to place the mothers of this nation on an equality with the fathers."

Weaver did not win the election, and Lease returned to Kansas to help the party win control of the state government the next year. She was nominated to run for the U.S. Senate, but she lost the chance to become the nation's first woman senator.

The next year Lease broke with the party. In 1895, she published a book that laid out her new vision for America. She proposed that the United States annex Canada, Cuba, and the West Indies; plant colonies in those areas; and establish free trade for the western hemisphere. She also believed that the government should take control of the railroad and telegraph systems, adopt free silver, and make political reforms.

In 1896, she refused to back the nomination of William Jennings Bryan, preferring William McKinley. She moved to New York, where she became a newspaper writer on politics and taught. She spent the remainder of her life pursuing various causes, including prohibition and women's suffrage. She supported Theodore Roosevelt in his 1912 Bull Moose campaign for the presidency. While still active, Lease was unable to achieve the influence she enjoyed in the 1890s.

Questions

1. How did Lease appeal to audiences?
2. What placed Lease in the forefront of women and politics after 1892?
3. Which of the positions taken by Lease in her book reflect Populist views?

Name _____ Date _____

After the Civil War, the United States was still a mostly rural nation. By the 1920s, it had become the leading industrial nation of the world. This immense change was caused by three major factors. Answer the questions for two of the factors.

➤ **Factor 1: Abundant Natural Resources**

1. Which resources played crucial roles in industrialization?	2. How did Edwin L. Drake help industry to acquire larger quantities of oil?	3. How did the Bessemer process allow better use of iron ore?	4. What new uses for steel were developed at this time?

➤ **Factor 2: Increasing Number of Inventions**

5. How did Thomas Alva Edison contribute to this development?	6. How did George Westinghouse contribute to it?	7. How did Christopher Sholes contribute?	8. How did Alexander Graham Bell contribute?

➤ **Factor 3: Expanding Urban Population**

Provided markets for new inventions and industrial goods	Provided a ready supply of labor for industry

Name _____ Date _____

GUIDED READING *The Age of the Railroads*

A. As you read, take notes to answer questions about the growth of the railroads.

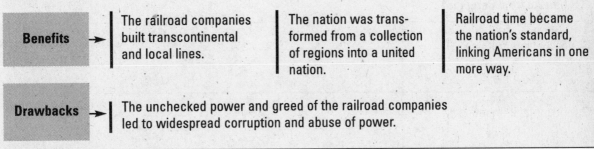

**Realizing that railroads were critical to the settlement of the West and the develop-
ment of the nation, the federal government made huge land grants and loans to the
railroad companies.**

| Benefits → | The railroad companies built transcontinental and local lines. | The nation was transformed from a collection of regions into a united nation. | Railroad time became the nation's standard, linking Americans in one more way. |

| Drawbacks → | The unchecked power and greed of the railroad companies led to widespread corruption and abuse of power. |

1. What problems did employees of the railroad companies face?	2. What was it like to live as a Pullman employee in the town of Pullman?
3. Who was involved in Crédit Mobilier, and what was the purpose of this company?	4. In what ways did the railroad companies use their power to hurt farmers?
5. Why didn't the decision in the *Munn* v. *Illinois* case succeed in checking the power of the railroads?	6. Why didn't the Interstate Commerce Act immediately limit the power of the railroads?

B. On the back of this paper, explain the importance to the United States of the
transcontinental railroad. Then, describe who **George M. Pullman** was and
why he is a significant historical figure.

CHAPTER 6

Section 3

GUIDED READING *Big Business and Labor*

As you read this section, answer the questions below about government's attempts to regulate big business.

   a. What is it?

   b. How did it help businesses such as the Carnegie Company and tycoons like Andrew Carnegie?

1. Vertical integration	a. b.
2. Horizontal integration	a. b.
3. Social Darwinism	a. b.
4. Monopoly	a. b.
5. Holding company	a. b.
6. Trust	a. b.

   c. How did it harm businesses such as Standard Oil and tycoons like John D. Rockefeller?

7. The perception of tycoons as "robber barons"	
8. Sherman Antitrust Act	

Name _____ Date _____

BUILDING VOCABULARY *A New Industrial Age*

A. Matching Match the definition in the second column with the term or name in the first column. Write the appropriate letter next to the word.

_____ 1. *Munn* v. *Illinois*   a. improved steel-making procedure

_____ 2. Andrew Carnegie   b. promoted business competition

_____ 3. Bessemer process   c. inventor of the telephone

_____ 4. Social Darwinism   d. merging of similar companies

_____ 5. horizontal integration   e. president of the AFL

_____ 6. Crédit Mobilier   f. gave states the right to regulate railroads

_____ 7. Alexander Graham Bell   g. steel magnate

_____ 8. Samuel Gompers   h. major railroad scandal

B. Completion Select the term or name that best completes the sentence.

George M. Pullman   John D. Rockefeller   Interstate Commerce Act
Sherman Antitrust Act   Christopher Sholes   vertical integration
transcontinental railroad   Thomas Alva Edison   Edwin L. Drake

1. Only after _____ successfully used a steam engine to drill oil did removing oil from below the earth's surface become practical.

2. The _____ reaffirmed the right of the federal government to supervise railroad activities.

3. _____ became one of the wealthiest and most powerful industrialists as head of the Standard Oil Company.

4. The Central Pacific and Union Pacific railroads met at Promontory Point, Utah, to create the nation's first _____.

5. _____ made it illegal to form trusts that interfered with free trade between states.

C. Writing Write a paragraph describing the emergence of the American labor movement using the following terms.

American Federation of Labor   Eugene V. Debs

Industrial Workers of the World   Mary Harris Jones

CHAPTER
6

Section 3

SKILLBUILDER PRACTICE *Creating Oral Presentations*

Were the captains of industry truly robber barons who corrupted American society? Were they industrial pioneers who benefited society by introducing innovative business techniques and gave back millions of dollars to charities and schools? Determine your position on this issue, then conduct research to support your position. Next, create an outline organizing facts and details around your main idea using the outline format below. Use the outline to create a brief oral presentation in support of your position. (See Skillbuilder Handbook, p. R36.)

I. Introduce Theme

    A. (supporting details) _____

    B. (supporting details) _____

II. Repeat Theme

    A. (supporting details) _____

    B. (supporting details) _____

III. Conclusion

    _____

    _____

    _____

CHAPTER
6
Section 1

RETEACHING ACTIVITY *The Expansion of Industry*

Matching

A. Match the following persons with their inventions or innovations.

_____ 1. William Le Baron Jenney   a. telephone

_____ 2. William Kelly   b. mass produced electricity

_____ 3. Thomas Alva Edison   c. steam engine oil drill

_____ 4. Alexander Graham Bell   d. typewriter

_____ 5. Christopher Sholes   e. steel-framed skyscraper

_____ 6. Edwin L. Drake   f. Bessemer process

Evaluating

B. Write *T* in the blank if the statement is true. If the statement is false, write *F* in the
blank and then write the corrected statement on the line below.

_____ 1. The major factors of the nation's industrial boom were a wealth of natural resources,
government support for business, and an abundance of farmland.

_____

_____ 2. Removing the carbon from iron produces a lighter, more flexible, and rust-resistant
metal known as steel.

_____

_____ 3. Railroad companies, which sought to build thousands of miles of track, became the
biggest customers for steel.

_____

_____ 4. By 1910, women made up only 5 percent of the nation's clerical workforce.

_____

_____ 5. The popularity of the automobile prompted entrepreneurs to transform more oil into
kerosene.

_____

CHAPTER
6
Section 2

RETEACHING ACTIVITY *The Age of the Railroads*

Sequencing

A. Number the events of the Railroad Era below in the order in which they occurred.

_____ 1. U.S. towns establish railroad time.

_____ 2. Congress passes the Interstate Commerce Act.

_____ 3. First transcontinental railroad created.

_____ 4. Pullman car workers launch violent strike.

_____ 5. Farmers form the Grange to address railroad abuses.

_____ 6. *Munn* v. *Illinois* gives states the right to regulate railroads.

_____ 7. Supreme Court rules ICC cannot set maximum railroad rates.

_____ 8. Railroads' financial problems prompt nationwide economic panic.

Finding Main Ideas

B. Choose the word that most accurately completes the sentences below.

Chinese	five	Granger laws
four	Standard Oil	financial companies
German	land grants	Irish

1. Recognizing how important railroads were for settling the West, the government made large
   _____ to the railroad companies.

2. The Central Pacific Railroad employed thousands of _____ immigrants, while numerous
   _____ immigrants worked for the Union Pacific Railroad.

3. Under railroad time, the United States was divided into _____ time zones.

4. Various measures enacted to regulate the railroads were known as _____.

5. By the end of the 19th century, a quarter of the nation's railroads had been taken over by _____.

CHAPTER
6
Section 3

RETEACHING ACTIVITY *Big Business and Labor*

Reading Comprehension

Choose the best answer for each item. Write the letter of your answer in the blank.

_____ 1. A corporation that did nothing but buy out the stock of other companies was known as a
      a. trust.
      b. holding company.
      c. Grange.
      d. monopoly.

_____ 2. John D. Rockefeller became a magnate of the
      a. oil industry.
      b. steel industry.
      c. railroad industry.
      d. cotton industry.

_____ 3. To improve their labor conditions, many industrial workers formed
      a. trusts.
      b. unions.
      c. holding companies.
      d. the Grange.

_____ 4. The Great Strike of 1877 involved workers for some of the nation's
      a. steel plants
      b. oil plants.
      c. railroads.
      d. textile mills.

_____ 5. The violent incident that turned much of the public against the labor movement was known as the
      a. Homestead Strike.
      b. Pullman Company Strike.
      c. Triangle Shirtwaist Factory fire.
      d. Haymarket Affair.

_____ 6. By World War I, membership in the American Federation of Labor was around
      a. 500,000.
      b. 1 million.
      c. 2 million.
      d. 3 million.

CHAPTER 6

GEOGRAPHY APPLICATION: HUMAN–ENVIRONMENT INTERACTION

The Changing Labor Force

Section 1

Directions: Read the paragraphs below and study the charts carefully. Then answer the questions that follow.

In 1859, the annual value of U.S. industrial production exceeded that of agricultural production for the first time. A shifting toward a predominantly urban population was occurring at the same time. This led to profound changes in occupations and income.

During the Civil War and immediately afterward, a broad spectrum of industries in the United States experienced incredible growth while fulfilling the product demands of the war and the expanding urban population. The increasing industrialization, though, brought grim working conditions. Employees often worked up to 12 hours a day, 6 days a week—with pay often less than $3 a day. Soon after 1870, industry over-expanded and over-produced, and wages fell.

Those still working on farms also had their problems. New farm machinery reduced the number of farm workers needed, even though the number of farms increased during the period. Then, after farm production greatly increased, prices for crops such as cotton and corn dropped in the 1870s when output exceeded demand.

The graphs below show how these changes affected those who worked on farms and those who did not.

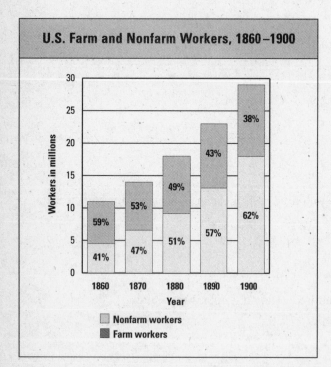

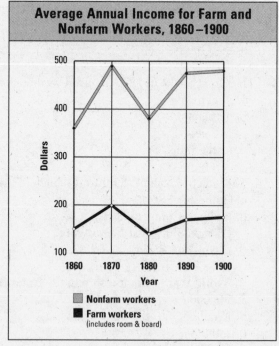

Interpreting Text and Visuals

1. About how many workers were there in the United States in 1860?

   _____

2. What percentage of the American labor force were farm workers in 1860?

   _____

3. About how many more farm workers were there in 1900 than in 1860? _____

   Explain why the percentage was less in 1900. _____

   _____

   _____

4. In what decade did the percentage of nonfarm workers first exceed the percentage
   of farm workers? _____

   What was the trend for the rest of the century? _____

   _____

5. About how much did the average farm worker earn in 1860? _____

6. How much did the average nonfarm worker earn in 1860? _____

   How much did he or she earn in 1900? _____

7. Explain what happened to wages during the 1870s. _____

   _____

   _____

   _____

8. Contrast the trend in number of workers between 1890 and 1900 with the trend
   for the same time period in workers' income. _____

   _____

   _____

   _____

CHAPTER 6

Section 1

PRIMARY SOURCE The Birth of the Telephone

While conducting telegraph experiments, Alexander Graham Bell and his assistant, Thomas A. Watson, made an important discovery—the telephone. As you read Watson's account, consider the inspiration that led to the birth of the telephone.

On the afternoon of June 2, 1875, we were hard at work on the same old job, testing some modification of the instruments. Things were badly out of tune that afternoon in the hot garret, not only the instruments, but, I fancy, my enthusiasm and my temper, though Bell was as energetic as ever. I had charge of the transmitters as usual, setting them squealing one after the other, while Bell was retuning the receiver springs one by one, pressing them against his ear as I have described. One of the transmitter springs I was attending to stopped vibrating and I plucked it to start it again.

It didn't start and I kept on plucking it, when suddenly I heard a shout from Bell in the next room, and then out he came with a rush, demanding, "What did you do then? Don't change anything. Let me see!" I showed him. It was very simple. The make-and-break points of the transmitter spring I was trying to start had become welded together, so that when I snapped the spring the circuit had remained unbroken while that strip of magnetized steel by its vibration over the pole of its magnet, was generating that marvelous conception of Bell's—a current of electricity that varied in density within hearing distance of that spring.

That undulatory current had passed through the connecting wire to the distant receiver which, fortunately, was a mechanism that could transform the current back into an extremely faint echo of the sound of the vibrating spring that had generated it, but what was still more fortunate, the right man had that mechanism at his ear during that fleeting moment, and instantly recognized the transcendent importance of that faint sound thus electrically transmitted. The shout I heard and his excited rush into my room were the result of that recognition. The speaking telephone was born at that moment. Bell knew perfectly well that the mechanism that could transmit all the complex vibrations of one sound could do the same for any sound, even that of speech.

That experiment showed him that the complex apparatus he had thought would be needed to accomplish that long-dreamed result was not at all

necessary, for here was an extremely simple mechanism operating in a perfectly obvious way, that could do it perfectly. All the experimenting that followed that discovery, up to the time the telephone was put into practical use was largely a matter of working out the details. . . .

You can well imagine that both our hearts were beating above the normal rate, while we were getting ready for the trial of the new instrument that evening. I got more satisfaction from the experiment than Mr. Bell did, for shout my best I could not make him hear me, but I could hear his voice and almost catch the words. I rushed upstairs and told him what I had heard. It was enough to show him that he was on the right track. . . .

It was not until the following March that I heard a complete and intelligible sentence. It made such an impression upon me that I wrote that first sentence in a book I have always preserved. The occasion had not been arranged and rehearsed as I suspect the sending of the first message over the Morse telegraph had been years before, for instead of that noble first telegraphic message—"What hath God Wrought?" the first message of the telephone was: "Mr. Watson, please come here, I want you." Perhaps, if Mr. Bell had realized that he was about to make a bit of history, he would have been prepared with a more sounding and interesting sentence.

from Richard B. Morris and James Woodress, eds., Voices from America's Past, Vol. 2, Backwoods Democracy to World Power (New York: Dutton, 1963), 219–221.

Research Options

1. Research the telephone's growth after Bell first exhibited it in public at the 1876 Philadelphia Centennial Exposition. Then prepare a brief oral report to share your findings.
2. Find a quote or saying that you think would have been a more "noble" first telephone message and share it with classmates.
3. Research Alexander Graham Bell's life. Write a brief biographical sketch and share it with the class.

PRIMARY SOURCE *from* "Wealth and Its Uses"
by Andrew Carnegie

Andrew Carnegie, the rags-to-riches industrialist, wrote books, lectures, and articles in which he praised American democracy and the free enterprise system. As you read this excerpt from an 1895 speech, consider his ideas about wealth and its uses.

You may be sure, gentlemen, that the question of the distribution of wealth is settling itself rapidly under present conditions, and settling itself in the right direction. The few rich are getting poorer, and the toiling masses are getting richer. Nevertheless, a few exceptional men may yet make fortunes, but these will be more moderate than in the past. This may not be quite as fortunate for the masses of the people as is now believed, because great accumulations of wealth in the hands of one enterprising man who still toils on are sometimes most productive of all the forms of wealth. . . .

But assuming that surplus wealth flows into the hands of a few men, what is their duty? How is the struggle for dollars to be lifted from the sordid atmosphere surrounding business and made a noble career? Now, wealth has hitherto been distributed in three ways: The first and chief one is by willing it at death to the family. Now, beyond bequeathing to those dependent upon one the revenue needful for modest and independent living, is such a use of wealth either right or wise?. . . It is not the good of the child which the millionaire parent considers when he makes these bequests, it is his own vanity; it is not affection for the child, it is self-glorification for the parent which is at the root of this injurious disposition of wealth. There is only one thing to be said for this mode, it furnishes one of the most efficacious means of rapid distribution of wealth ever known.

There is a second use of wealth, less common than the first, which is not so injurious to the community, but which should bring no credit to the testator. Money is left by millionaires to public institutions when they must relax their grasp upon it. There is no grace, and can be no blessing, in giving what cannot be withheld. It is no gift, because it is not cheerfully given, but only granted at the stern summons of death. The miscarriage of these bequests, the litigation connected with them, and the manner in which they are frittered away seem to prove that the Fates do not regard them with a

kindly eye. We are never without a lesson that the only mode of producing lasting good by giving large sums of money is for the millionaire to give as close attention to its distribution during his life as he did to its acquisition. . . .

The third use, and the only noble use of surplus wealth, is this: That it be regarded as a sacred trust, to be administered by its possessor, into whose hands it flows, for the highest good of the people. Man does not live by bread alone, and five or ten cents a day more revenue scattered over thousands would produce little or no good. Accumulated into a great fund and expended as Mr. Cooper expended it for the Cooper Institute, it establishes something that will last for generations. It will educate the brain, the spiritual part of man. It furnishes a ladder upon which the aspiring poor may climb, and there is no use whatever, gentlemen, trying to help people who do not help themselves. You cannot push any one up a ladder unless he be willing to climb a little himself. When you stop boosting, he falls, to his injury. Therefore, I have often said, and I now repeat, that the day is coming, and already we see its dawn, in which the man who dies possessed of millions of available wealth which was free and in his hands ready to be distributed will die disgraced. . . .

from Andrew Carnegie, "Wealth and Its Uses," January 1895. Reprinted in Louis M. Hacker, ed. *The Shaping of the American Tradition* (New York: Columbia University Press, 1947), 807–810.

Discussion Questions

1. What did Carnegie say are three ways to use wealth?
2. Which of the three uses did he endorse?
3. From what you know about Carnegie's life, did he live up to his own philosophy of wealth and its uses? Why or why not? Cite evidence from your textbook to support your opinion.

CHAPTER 6

Section 3

PRIMARY SOURCE *from* **The History of the Standard Oil Company**

Journalist Ida M. Tarbell exposed John D. Rockefeller's ruthless building of Standard Oil Company, the first major industrial monopoly in the United States. As you read this excerpt from Tarbell's book, think about how Rockefeller controlled the oil industry.

To know every detail of the oil trade, to be able to reach at any moment its remotest point, to control even its weakest factor—this was John D. Rockefeller's ideal of doing business. It seemed to be an intellectual necessity for him to be able to direct the course of any particular gallon of oil from the moment it gushed from the earth until it went into the lamp of a housewife. There must be nothing—nothing in his great machine he did not know to be working right. It was to complete this ideal, to satisfy this necessity, that he undertook, late in the seventies [1870s], to organize the oil markets of the world, as he had already organized oil refining and oil transporting. Mr. Rockefeller was driven to this new task of organization not only by his own curious intellect; he was driven to it by that thing so abhorrent to his mind—competition. If, as he claimed, the oil business belonged to him, and if, as he had announced, he was prepared to refine all the oil that men would consume, it followed as a corollary that the markets of the world belonged to him. . . .

When Mr. Rockefeller began to gather the oil markets into his hands he had a task whose field was literally the world, for already, in 1871, the year before he first appeared as an important factor in the oil trade, refined oil was going into every civilized country of the globe. Of the five and a half million barrels of crude oil produced that year, the world used five millions, over three and a half of which went to foreign lands. This was the market which had been built up in the first ten years of business by the men who had developed the oil territory and invented the processes of refining and transporting, and this was the market, still further developed, of course, that Mr. Rockefeller inherited when he succeeded in corralling the refining and transporting of oil. It was this market he proceeded to organize.

The process of organization seems to have been natural and highly intelligent. The entire country was buying refined oil for illumination. Many refiners had their own agents out looking for markets; others sold to wholesale dealers, or jobbers, who placed trade with local dealers, usually grocers. Mr. Rockefeller's business was to replace independent agents and jobbers by his own employees. The United States was mapped out and agents appointed over these great divisions. Thus, a certain portion of the Southwest—including Kansas, Missouri, Arkansas and Texas—the Waters-Pierce Oil Company, of St. Louis, Missouri, had charge of; a portion of the South—including Kentucky, Tennessee and Mississippi—Chess, Carley and Company, of Louisville, Kentucky, had charge of. These companies in turn divided their territory into sections, and put the subdivisions in the charge of local agents. These local agents had stations where oil was received and stored, and from which they and their salesmen carried on their campaigns. This system, inaugurated in the seventies, has been developed until now the Standard Oil Company of each state has its own marketing department, whose territory is divided and watched over in the above fashion. The entire oil-buying territory of the country is thus covered by local agents reporting to division headquarters. These report in turn to the head of the state marketing department, and his reports go to the general marketing headquarters in New York. . . .

But the Standard Oil agents were not sent into a territory back in the seventies simply to sell all the oil they could by efficient service and aggressive pushing; they were sent there to sell all the oil that was bought. "The coal-oil business belongs to us," was Mr. Rockefeller's motto, and from the beginning of his campaign in the markets his agents accepted and acted on that principle. If a dealer bought but a barrel of oil a year, it must be from Mr. Rockefeller.

from Ida M. Tarbell, *The History of the Standard Oil Company* (New York: Norton, 1966), 110–112.

Discussion Questions

1. How did Rockefeller set out to acquire control of the oil industry?
2. Do you think Rockefeller deserved to be called a "robber baron?" Why or why not?

CHAPTER

6

Section 3

PRIMARY SOURCE Labor Poster

In 1905 radical unionists and socialists formed the Industrial Workers of the World (IWW) to organize unskilled and semiskilled workers such as western miners, migrant farm workers, lumbermen, and some eastern textile workers. IWW members, known as Wobblies, pasted small posters like this one on fence posts or in railroad boxcars to call attention to their cause. What impression of the IWW do you get from this poster?

Library of Congress

Discussion Questions

1. What message do the images and slogans included in this poster convey to you?

2. What do you find most persuasive about this poster? Why?

3. Why do you think IWW posters were often called "silent agitators"?

CHAPTER **6**

Section 2

LITERATURE SELECTION *from* "The Bride Comes to Yellow Sky" by Stephen Crane

In this excerpt from Stephen Crane's short story, Jack Potter and his new wife travel by train from San Antonio, Texas, to the frontier town of Yellow Sky. As you read this excerpt, pay attention to Crane's rich description of trains in the 1800s and to the newlyweds' reaction to rail travel.

The great Pullman was whirling onward with such dignity of motion that a glance from the window seemed simply to prove that the plains of Texas were pouring eastward. Vast flats of green grass, dull-hued spaces of mesquit and cactus, little groups of frame houses, woods of light and tender trees, all were sweeping into the east, sweeping over the horizon, a precipice.

A newly married pair had boarded this coach at San Antonio. The man's face was reddened from many days in the wind and sun, and a direct result of his new black clothes was that his brick-coloured hands were constantly performing in a most conscious fashion. From time to time he looked down respectfully at his attire. He sat with a hand on each knee, like a man waiting in a barber's shop. The glances he devoted to other passengers were furtive and shy.

The bride was not pretty, nor was she very young. She wore a dress of blue cashmere, with small reservations of velvet here and there, and with steel buttons abounding. She continually twisted her head to regard her puff sleeves, very stiff, straight, and high. They embarrassed her. It was quite apparent that she had cooked, and that she expected to cook, dutifully. The blushes caused by the careless scrutiny of some passengers as she had entered the car were strange to see upon this plain, under-class countenance, which was drawn in placid, almost emotionless lines.

They were evidently very happy. "Ever been in a parlour-car before?" he asked, smiling with delight.

"No," she answered; "I never was. It's fine, ain't it?"

"Great! And then after a while we'll go forward to the diner, and get a big lay-out. Finest meal in

Her eyes opened wider as she contemplated the sea-green figured velvet, the shining brass, silver, and glass, the wood that gleamed as darkly brilliant as the surface of a pool of oil.

the world. Charge a dollar."

"Oh, do they?" cried the bride. "Charge a dollar? Why, that's too much—for us—ain't it, Jack?"

"Not this trip, anyhow," he answered bravely. "We're going to go the whole thing."

Later he explained to her about the trains. "You see, it's a thousand miles from one end of Texas to the other; and this train runs right across it, and never stops but four times." He had the pride of an owner. He pointed out to her the dazzling fittings of the coach; and in truth her eyes opened wider as she contemplated the sea-green figured velvet, the shining brass, silver, and glass, the wood that gleamed as darkly brilliant as the surface of a pool of oil. At one end a bronze figure sturdily held a support for a separated chamber, and at convenient places on the ceiling were frescos in olive and silver.

To the minds of the pair, their surroundings reflected the glory of their marriage that morning in San Antonio; this was the environment of their new estate; and the man's face in particular beamed with an elation that made him appear ridiculous to the negro porter. This individual at times surveyed them from afar with an amused and superior grin. On other occasions he bullied them with skill in ways that did not make it exactly plain to them that they were being bullied. He subtly used all the manners of the most unconquerable kind of snobbery. He oppressed them; but of this oppression they had small knowledge, and they speedily forgot that infrequently a number of travellers covered them with stares of derisive enjoyment. Historically there was supposed to be something infinitely humorous in their situation.

"We are due in Yellow Sky at 3:42," he said,

looking tenderly into her eyes.

"Oh, are we?" she said, as if she had not been aware of it. To evince surprise at her husband's statement was part of her wifely amiability. She took from a pocket a little silver watch; and as she held it before her, and stared at it with a frown of attention, the new husband's face shone.

"I bought it in San Anton' from a friend of mine," he told her gleefully.

"It's seventeen minutes past twelve," she said, looking up at him with a kind of shy and clumsy coquetry. A passenger, noting this play, grew excessively sardonic, and winked at himself in one of the numerous mirrors.

At last they went to the dining-car. Two rows of negro waiters, in glowing white suits, surveyed their entrance with the interest, and also the equanimity, of men who had been forewarned. The pair fell to the lot of a waiter who happened to feel pleasure in steering them through their meal. He viewed them with the manner of a fatherly pilot, his countenance radiant with benevolence. The patronage, entwined with the ordinary deference, was not plain to them. And yet, as they returned to their coach, they showed in their faces a sense of escape.

To the left, miles down a purple slope, was a little ribbon of mist where moved the keening Rio Grande. The train was approaching it at an angle, and the apex was Yellow Sky. Presently it was apparent that, as the distance from Yellow Sky grew shorter, the husband became commensurately restless. His brick-red hands were more insistent in their prominence. Occasionally he was even rather absent-minded and far-away when the bride leaned forward and addressed him.

As a matter of truth, Jack Potter was beginning to find the shadow of a deed weigh upon him like a leaden slab. He, the town marshal of Yellow Sky, a man known, liked, and feared in his corner, a prominent person, had gone to San Antonio to meet a girl he believed he loved, and there, after the usual prayers, had actually induced her to marry him, without consulting Yellow Sky for any part of the transaction. He was now bringing his bride before an innocent and unsuspecting community.

He knew full well that his marriage was an important thing to his town. It could only be exceeded by the burning of the new hotel.

Of course people in Yellow Sky married as it pleased them, in accordance with a general custom; but such was Potter's thought of his duty to his friends, or of their idea of his duty, or of an unspoken form which does not control men in these matters, that he felt he was heinous. He had committed an extraordinary crime. Face to face with this girl in San Antonio, and spurred by his sharp impulse, he had gone headlong over all the social hedges. At San Antonio he was like a man hidden in the dark. A knife to sever any friendly duty, any form, was easy to his hand in that remote city. But the hour of Yellow Sky—the hour of daylight—was approaching.

He knew full well that his marriage was an important thing to his town. It could only be exceeded by the burning of the new hotel. His friends could not forgive him. Frequently he had reflected on the advisability of telling them by telegraph, but a new cowardice had been upon him. He feared to do it. And now the train was hurrying him toward a scene of amazement, glee, and reproach. He glanced out of the window at the line of haze swinging slowly in toward the train.

Yellow Sky had a kind of brass band, which played painfully, to the delight of the populace. He laughed without heart as he thought of it. If the citizens could dream of this prospective arrival with his bride, they would parade the band at the station and escort them, amid cheers and laughing congratulations, to his adobe home.

He resolved that he would use all the devices of speed and plainscraft in making the journey from the station to his house. Once within that safe citadel, he could issue some sort of vocal bulletin, and then not go among the citizens until they had time to wear off a little of their enthusiasm.

The bride looked anxiously at him. "What's worrying you, Jack?"

He laughed again. "I'm not worrying, girl; I'm only thinking of Yellow Sky."

She flushed in comprehension.

A sense of mutual guilt invaded their minds and developed a finer tenderness. They looked at each other with eyes softly aglow. But Potter often laughed the same nervous laugh; the flush upon the bride's face seemed quite permanent.

The traitor to the feelings of Yellow Sky narrowly watched the speeding landscape. "We're nearly there," he said.

Presently the porter came and announced the proximity of Potter's home. He held a brush in his hand, and, with all his airy superiority gone, he brushed Potter's new clothes as the latter slowly turned this way and that way. Potter fumbled out a coin and gave it to the porter, as he had seen others do. It was a heavy and muscle-bound business, as that of a man shoeing his first horse.

The porter took their bag, and as the train began to slow they moved forward to the hooded platform of the car. Presently the two engines and their long string of coaches rushed into the station of Yellow Sky.

"They have to take water here," said Potter, from a constricted throat and in mournful cadence, as one announcing death. Before the train stopped his eye had astonished to see there was none upon it but the station-agent, who, with a slightly hurried and anxious air, was walking toward the water-tanks. When the train had halted, the porter alighted first, and placed in position a little temporary step.

"Come on, girl," said Potter, hoarsely. As he helped her down they each laughed on a false note. He took the bag from the negro, and bade his wife cling to his arm. As they slunk rapidly away, his hang-dog glance perceived that they were unloading the two trunks, and also that the station-agent, far ahead near the baggage-car, had turned and was running toward him, making gestures. He laughed, and groaned as he laughed, when he noted the first effect of his marital bliss upon Yellow Sky. He gripped his wife's arm firmly to his side, and they fled. Behind them the porter stood, chuckling fatuously. . . .

Potter and his bride walked sheepishly and with speed. Sometimes they laughed together shame-facedly and low.

"Next corner, dear," he said finally.

They put forth the efforts of a pair walking bowed against a strong wind. Potter was about to raise his finger to point the first appearance of the new home when, as they circled the corner, they came face to face with a man in a maroon-coloured shirt, who was feverishly pushing cartridges into a large revolver. Upon the instant the man dropped his revolver to the ground and, like lightning,

The two men faced each other at a distance of three paces. He of the revolver smiled with a new and quiet ferocity.

whipped another from its holster. The second weapon was aimed at the bridegroom's chest.

There was a silence. Potter's mouth seemed to be merely a grave for his tongue. He exhibited an instinct to at once loosen his arm from the woman's grip, and he dropped the bag to the sand. As for the bride, her face had gone as yellow as old cloth. She was a slave to hideous rites, gazing at the apparitional snake.

The two men faced each other at a distance of three paces. He of the revolver smiled with a new and quiet ferocity.

"Tried to sneak up on me," he said. "Tried to sneak up on me!" His eyes grew more baleful. As Potter made a slight movement, the man thrust his revolver ven-omously forward. "No; don't you do it, Jack Potter. Don't you move an eyelash. The time has come for me to settle with you, and I'm goin' to do it my own way, and loaf along with no interferin'. So if you don't want a gun bent on you, just mind what I tell you."

Potter looked at his enemy. "I ain't got a gun on me, Scratchy," he said. "Honest, I ain't." He was stiffening and steadying, but yet somewhere at the back of his mind a vision of the Pullman floated; the sea-green figured velvet, the shining brass, silver, and glass, the wood that gleamed as darkly brilliant as the surface of a pool of oil—all the glory of the marriage, the environment of the new estate. "You know I fight when it comes to fighting, Scratchy Wilson; but I ain't got a gun on me. You'll have to do all the shootin' yourself."

Activity Options

1. Hold a small-group discussion in which you compare and contrast train travel today with that of the description in this excerpt from "The Bride Comes to Yellow Sky."
2. Draw a sketch of a Pullman car based on Crane's description. Then label your sketch and display it in the classroom.
3. Imagine that you are Jack Potter or his bride. Write a postcard to a friend in which you describe your trip from San Antonio to Yellow Sky. Share your postcard with your classmates.

CHAPTER 6

Section 3

AMERICAN LIVES Andrew Carnegie

Hard Worker, Generous Patron

"Make no effort to increase fortune, but spend the surplus each year for benevolent purposes. Cast aside business for ever, except for others."— Andrew Carnegie, memo to himself (1868)

Andrew Carnegie showed how hard work and shrewd thinking can be used to build a fortune. He then showed how that fortune can be used to benefit others.

Born in Scotland, Carnegie (1835–1919) emigrated to the United States with his family when his father could no longer find work. They settled near Lake Erie, and Carnegie—only 13—began working in a textile mill. He regretted not having had the chance for an education but found a substitute. He took advantage of the offer of a local man who provided access to his personal library to any working boys in the area. Carnegie borrowed more books than anyone else. He maintained his wide reading all his life, using it to make himself entertaining at social gatherings.

His main goal was to rise on the job, though. Carnegie soon became a telegraph messenger. He gained attention by learning to decipher messages by sound and was promoted to telegraph operator. Soon a top manager in the Pennsylvania Railroad hired him as his personal secretary. Carnegie was only 18.

He advanced through many positions at the railroad, eventually taking his former boss's job as head of the Pittsburgh division by age 30. He helped organize troop transportation and telegraph systems used in the Civil War. After the war, Carnegie resigned from the railroad and started his own company to build iron bridges. Railroad contacts helped him win business, and his company thrived.

By 1873, Carnegie was ready to launch a new business: making steel. He formed the Carnegie Company and led it to success. With strong organizational skills and a knack for spotting and promoting talent, Carnegie built a huge empire. He was committed to improving technology whenever possible. Shrewdly, he chose recessions as the time to improve his factories. The improvements cost less then, and when the economy improved he was ready to produce steel more cheaply than competitors. The strategy worked: his company earned $40 million in prof-

its in 1900, of which $25 million was his.

Carnegie wrote and spoke, hoping to spread his ideas about success and the responsibilities of the successful. He told students at a Pittsburgh business school how to succeed: "The rising man must do something exceptional, and beyond the range of his special department."

In 1889, he published an article called "Wealth," also known as "The Gospel of Wealth." In his essay, Carnegie argued that after accumulating a fortune, a wealthy man had a duty: he should use some of his money for "the improvement of mankind." He sold his steel company in 1901 and spent most of the rest of his life fulfilling this "gospel."

He donated about $350 million. More than a third went to endow the Carnegie Corporation, which could continue his generosity beyond his death. He gave some $20 million to U.S. colleges and another $10 million to Scottish universities. He created the Carnegie Institute of Pittsburgh, which had a library, an art museum, and a music hall. He also created the Carnegie Institute of Washington for basic research in science. He also gave $60 million to create more than 3,000 public libraries.

Carnegie lost some of his good name in the Homestead strike of 1892. Steel workers were shut out of one of his plants and lost their jobs. Although he did not direct the company's actions, he did nothing to help the situation, which cost him public support. Long after, though, he was remembered as a generous benefactor.

Questions

1. What evidence do you find that Carnegie followed his own advice in rising to the top?
2. Do you agree with Carnegie's "gospel of wealth"? Why or why not?
3. What do you consider the most important example of Carnegie's generosity?

CHAPTER
6
Section 3

AMERICAN LIVES Mary Harris "Mother" Jones
Labor's Inspiration

"The workers asked only for bread and a shortening of long hours of toil. The agitators gave them visions. The police gave them clubs."—The Autobiography of Mother Jones (1925)

Mary Harris "Mother" Jones was a short woman whose grandmotherly looks hid a steely determination and a fiery tongue. She put both to use in her quest for workers' rights.

Mary Harris was born in Ireland in 1830 and emigrated with her family to Canada when she was 11. They settled in the United States some years later, and she worked at teaching and dressmaking. In 1861, she married George Jones, an iron worker and devoted union man. They had four children, but tragedy struck. Jones and all the children died in an 1867 Memphis yellow-fever epidemic. Later Mary Jones remembered bitterly that the victims of the epidemic "were mainly among the poor and the workers. The rich and the well-to-do fled the city." She moved to Chicago to work as a dressmaker again—and then lost everything in the great fire that destroyed much of that city in 1871.

Wandering the devastated city, Jones stopped into a union meeting hall. It belonged to the Knights of Labor, a union that tried to organize both skilled and unskilled workers. She began to attend regularly, and she soon fully embraced the cause. At one meeting, she entered in a lively debate with a Knights of Labor official. He asked to speak to her afterwards and was impressed by her awareness of labor issues. He was Terence Powderly, soon to be the head of the Knights. They became friends, and Jones became a dedicated union organizer and agitator.

Her strength was not organizational skills but inspiration. "No matter what impossible ideas she brought up," one observer wrote, "she made the miners think she and they together could do anything." Despite her small size, she was a strong and vocal union advocate. Workers affectionately called her "Mother" Jones.

Jones crisscrossed the country, helping workers wherever she thought she was needed. She supported striking railroad workers in Pittsburgh in 1877 and in Birmingham, Alabama, in 1894. She worked for miners in Pennsylvania from 1900 to 1902, in Colorado from 1903 to 1906, in Idaho in 1906, and back in Colorado in 1913 to 1914. Then she moved to New York City to support garment workers and streetcar workers.

She also staged clever events. During the 1902 coal strike, she led miners' wives to march to a mine's gates as nonstriking workers arrived for work. The women persuaded these miners to join the strike afterall. She planned another move the following year—a 22-day march of child workers from Pennsylvania to New York. Her goal was to show President Theodore Roosevelt the suffering caused by child labor. The march lost strength over time, and the president refused to see her. But the event won newspaper space that publicized the problem.

Revered by workers, she was feared and hated by management and law-enforcement officials. A West Virginia prosecutor called her "the most dangerous woman in America" because she could rouse workers to act. She was arrested many times and in 1913 was convicted on a trumped-up charge of conspiracy to murder that was later overturned.

She continued the fight throughout her long life, joining the steel strike of 1919 and helping coal miners in 1923—at age 93. In 1930, Jones received many honors on reaching 100. One congratulatory note came from millionaire businessman—and long-time foe—John D. Rockefeller. He praised Jones for "loyalty to your ideals." Before the end of that year, though, Jones died. She was taken to Illinois, where she was laid to rest in the Union Miners Cemetery along with those who died in an 1898 mine riot.

Questions

1. Do you think that Jones's appearance helped her or hurt her in the effort to unionize?
2. Why did getting publicity help the union cause?
3. Why did management and law-enforcement officials fear Jones?

Name _____ Date _____

GUIDED READING *The New Immigrants*

A. As you read about people who immigrated to the United States in the late 19th and early 20th centuries, write notes to answer the questions below.

Immigrants from . . .	What were some of the countries they came from?	What reasons did they often have for coming to the U.S.?	Where did they often enter the U.S.?
1. Southern and Eastern Europe			❐ Ellis Island ❐ Angel Island ❐ Southeastern U.S. ❐ Southwestern U.S.
2. Asia			❐ Ellis Island ❐ Angel Island ❐ Southeastern U.S. ❐ Southwestern U.S.
3. Caribbean Islands and Central America			❐ Ellis Island ❐ Angel Island ❐ Southeastern U.S. ❐ Southwestern U.S.

B. In each box below, identify an important difference that tended to exist between native-born Americans and some or all of the new immigrants around the turn of the century.

Native-Born	New Immigrants

C. On the back of this paper, explain the purposes of the **Chinese Exclusion Act** and the **Gentlemen's Agreement.**

Name _____ Date _____

GUIDED READING *The Challenges of Urbanization*

A. As you read about the rapid growth of American cities in the late 19th and early 20th centuries, take notes to answer the questions below.

The People	Why was each group drawn to cities in the Northeast and Midwest?
1. Immigrants	
2. Farmers	
3. African Americans	

The Problems	What was done in response to each problem?
4. Lack of safe and efficient transportation	
5. Unsafe drinking water	
6. Lack of sanitation	
7. Fire hazards	
8. Crime	

B. On the back of this paper, define **urbanization.** Then, explain how the **Social Gospel movement, settlement houses,** and **Jane Addams** were involved in efforts to solve the problems of urbanization.

Name _____ Date _____

CHAPTER
7

Section 3

GUIDED READING *Politics in the Gilded Age*

A. As you read this section, fill out the chart below by writing answers to questions about the Gilded Age.

1876	Rutherford B. Hayes elected president →	1. What was Hayes's position on civil service reform? What did he do to promote it?
1880	James A. Garfield elected president →	2. In the debate over civil service reform, did Garfield seem to favor the Stalwarts or the reformers?
1881	Garfield assassinated; Chester A. Arthur assumes the presidency →	3. What position did Arthur take on civil service reform, and what did he do to support it?
1883	Pendleton Act passed →	4. What did the Pendleton Act do?
1884	Grover Cleveland elected president →	5. What was Cleveland's position on tariffs, and what did he do to promote this position?
1888	Benjamin Harrison elected president →	6. What was Harrison's position on tariffs, and what did he do to support that stand?
1892	Cleveland reelected president →	7. What happened to tariffs during Cleveland's second presidency?
1897	William McKinley elected president →	8. What happened to tariffs during McKinley's presidency?

B. On the back of this paper, define **political machine** and describe how it worked.

Name _____ Date _____

CHAPTER
7

BUILDING VOCABULARY *Immigration and Urbanization*

A. Evaluating Write *T* in the blank if the statement is true. If the statement is false, write *F* in the blank and then write the corrected statement on the line below.

_____ 1. As part of the Gentleman's Agreement, China's government agreed to limit immigration of unskilled workers to the United States.

_____

_____ 2. The Americanization movement was designed to assimilate immigrants into American culture.

_____

_____ 3. Settlement houses, multifamily urban dwellings, were often overcrowded and unsanitary.

_____

_____ 4. The Pendleton Civil Service Act required that appointments to federal jobs be based on a merit system.

_____

_____ 5. Grover Cleveland, who won the presidency in 1884, supported lower tariffs.

_____

B. Completion Select the term or name that best completes the sentence.

James Garfield	nativism	Social Gospel movement
Angel Island	Ellis Island	Rutherford B. Hayes
melting pot	urbanization	Chinese Exclusion Act

1. _____ promoted civil service reform by naming independents to his cabinet and investigating the nation's corrupt custom houses.

2. _____ preached salvation through service to the poor.

3. Most European immigrants made their way into the United States through _____.

4. With the rise in immigration throughout the late 1800s and the mixing of so many different cultures, the United States became known as a _____.

5. _____, or favoritism toward native-born Americans, gave rise to anti-immigrant groups.

C. Writing Write a paragraph describing the politics of the Gilded Age using the following terms.

political machine   **graft**   **Boss Tweed**   **patronage**

Name _____ Date _____

SKILLBUILDER PRACTICE *Creating Maps*

Using a U.S. atlas as well as the information from the map on page 255, create a map in the space below of the United States around 1900 that depicts the following information: the locations of Ellis Island and Angel Island; those states with immigrant populations of 100,000 or greater, 200,000 or greater, 300,000 or greater, 400,000 or greater, 700,000 or greater, and 1 million or greater. Depict the information in a way that is clear and easy to understand (Shading the states different colors based on their immigrant populations, for example). Be sure to include a key or legend explaining all colors, symbols, or shading. (See Skillbuilder Handbook, p. R32.)

SKILLBUILDER PRACTICE *Interpreting Political Cartoons*

Section 3

The corruption and graft exhibited by numerous politicians during the Gilded Age did not go unnoticed by the nation's political cartoonists. Examine the political cartoon below and then answer the questions that follow. (See Skillbuilder Handbook, p. R24.)

1. What is the subject of the cartoon?

_____

2. From where is the politician stealing money? How is he doing it?

_____

3. What is the meaning of the cut "red tape"?

_____

4. What point is the cartoonist trying to make?

_____

Name _____ Date _____

CHAPTER 7

Section 1

RETEACHING ACTIVITY *The New Immigrants*

Reading Comprehension

A. Choose the word that most accurately completes the sentences below.

German	religious	air plane
literacy test	Jews	Chinese
steamship	political	Swedish

1. Many _____ fled Russia to America as a result of pogroms, or organized attacks, against them.

2. _____ immigrants helped build the nation's railroads.

3. President Cleveland vetoed a bill requiring a _____ for immigrants.

4. Nativists objected to immigrants' _____ beliefs as well as their ethnic backgrounds.

5. By the 1870s, almost all immigrants traveled by _____.

Summarizing

B. Complete the chart shown here by summarizing the Chinese Exclusion Act and the Gentleman's Agreement.

Chinese Exclusion Act	Gentlemen's Agreement

CHAPTER
7
Section 2

RETEACHING ACTIVITY *The Challenges of Urbanization*

Finding Main Ideas

Choose the best answer for each item. Write the letter of your answer in the blank.

_____ 1. Many immigrants flocked to the nation's cities because of
    a. quality schools.
    b. steady jobs.
    c. convenient shopping.
    d. a rich cultural atmosphere.

_____ 2. Among the many Southern farmers who moved to the cities to find jobs was a large group of
    a. Native Americans.
    b. African Americans.
    c. Dutch.
    d. Scots-Irish.

_____ 3. In 1873, San Francisco unveiled a new mode of transportation known as the
    a. automobile.
    b. airplane.
    c. street car.
    d. bicycle.

_____ 4. Settlement houses were run largely by
    a. women.
    b. African Americans.
    c. immigrants.
    d. political bosses.

_____ 5. The co-founder of Hull House in Chicago was
    a. Jane Addams.
    b. Janie Porter Barrett.
    c. Jacob Riis.
    d. Elizabeth Cady Stanton.

_____ 6. One thing that most urban dwellers did not have to worry about was
    a. overcrowded conditions.
    b. poor sanitation
    c. crime and fire
    d. access to transportation.

CHAPTER
7
Section 3

RETEACHING ACTIVITY *Politics in the Gilded Age*

Sequencing

A. Number the events of the Gilded Age below in the order in which they occurred.

_____ 1. Law officials break up the Tweed Ring.

_____ 2. President James Garfield is assassinated.

_____ 3. Congress passes Pendleton Civil Service Act.

_____ 4. Boss Tweed becomes head of Tammany Hall.

_____ 5. McKinley Tarriff raises tariffs to highest level yet.

_____ 6. Rutherford B. Hayes becomes president.

Finding Main Ideas

B. Choose the word that most accurately completes the sentences below.

Thomas Nast	kickbacks	Grover Cleveland
business	immigrants	farming
Roscoe Conkling	Chester Arthur	African Americans

1. Elected president in 1884 and again in 1892, _____ was the only president to serve two nonconsecutive terms.

2. _____ was the political cartoonist who helped arouse public outrage against the Tweed Ring.

3. Political machines won loyal support from _____ for helping them find housing and jobs.

4. Many political machines enriched themselves with _____, or illegal payments for their services.

5. The _____ community favored high tariffs because they protected domestic industries from foreign competition.

Name _____ Date _____

GEOGRAPHY APPLICATION: HUMAN–ENVIRONMENT INTERACTION
Industry and Urban Growth

Directions: Read the paragraphs below and study the charts carefully. Then answer the questions that follow.

In the late 1800s, the United States experienced not only remarkable industrial growth but also a shift in the types of goods it produced.

New technology contributed greatly to the change in goods. For example, the Bessemer process for making steel from iron had been invented. For the first time, steel could be made cheaply in large quantities. As a result, steel—which lasts up to twenty times longer than iron—became increasingly popular.

Population movement related to immigration and rural migration also occurred in the late 1800s. Industrialized urban areas in the Northwest and Midwest offered jobs to immigrants and to former farmers.

Net Worth of the Ten Largest Manufacturing Industries

1879		1909	
INDUSTRY	($ Millions)	INDUSTRY	($ Millions)
Textiles and their products	$ 602	Food and drink	$ 2,935
Food and drink	498	Textiles and their products	2,550
Forest products	361	Iron and steel and their products	2,411
Iron and steel and their products	318	Machinery	1,860
Machinery	242	Forest products	1,767
Leather products	157	Chemicals	1,280
Chemicals	137	Cotton goods	860
Metal other than iron	86	Stone and glass products	705
Stone and glass products	83	Leather products	659
Printing and publishing	80	Printing and publishing	611
All manufacturing	$2,718	All manufacturing	$16,937

Urban Growth

	INCORPORATED PLACES, 2,500 AND OVER		INCORPORATED PLACES, 100,000 AND OVER		INCORPORATED PLACES, 1,000,000 AND OVER	
YEAR	NUMBER	PERCENTAGE OF TOTAL POPULATION	NUMBER	PERCENTAGE OF TOTAL POPULATION	NUMBER	PERCENTAGE OF TOTAL POPULATION
1880	930	28.2	20	12.3	1	2.4
1890	1,348	35.1	28	15.4	3	5.8
1900	1,737	39.7	38	18.7	3	8.4
1910	2,262	45.7	50	22.0	3	9.2

Interpreting Text and Visuals

1. Which manufacturing industry added the most value to the economy in 1879?

   _____

   in 1909? _____

2. Which industry appears on the list for 1909 that was not there for 1879? _____

   Which industry fell three rankings from 1879 to 1909? _____

3. How does the worth of the tenth-ranked industry in 1909 compare with the top-
   ranked industry of just thirty years earlier? _____

   _____

   How many times greater is the worth of all manufacturing in 1909 than the worth
   of all manufacturing thirty years earlier?_____

4. What might explain the increase in the rankings of stone, glass, iron, and steel and
   the decline in rankings of forest products and leather products? _____

   _____

5. The iron and steel industry increased only one ranking from 1879 to 1909. Yet iron
   and steel could fairly be called one of the industries that had risen dramatically
   during that time period. Explain.

   _____

   _____

6. What percentage of the population lived in incorporated places (towns and cities)
   having a population of between 100,000 and 1 million in 1880? _____

   in 1910? _____

7. What was the increase in the percentage of the country's total population in all
   incorporated places of more than 2,500 between the years 1880 and 1910?_____

   _____

8. The number of incorporated cities over 1,000,000 stayed the same from 1890 to
   1910, yet their percentage of the total population rose. Explain. _____

   _____

OUTLINE MAP *The Urbanization of America*

A. Review the maps of the political and physical features of the United States on pages A6–7 and A8–9. Then label the following bodies of water and cities on the accompanying outline map.

Bodies of Water		Cities
Pacific Ocean	Lake Michigan	Los Angeles
Atlantic Ocean	Lake Erie	San Francisco
Mississippi River	Lake Superior	Minneapolis
Lake Ontario	Lake Huron	

B. After completing the map, use it to answer the following questions.

1. In 1890, was population density greater east or west of the Mississippi River?_____

2. What was the population density of most of the land in Nevada, Wyoming, Arizona, and Oklahoma? _____

3. Which four states bordering the Great Lakes had no areas of fewer than two people per square mile? _____

4. Name the only five states entirely east of the Mississippi River that had areas of population density of fewer than two people per square mile. _____

_____

Name the only three states entirely west of the Mississippi River that had no areas of population density of fewer than two people per square mile. _____

_____

5. What did the area bordering Lake Superior lack in population density that each of the other Great Lakes had? _____

6. Describe the 1890 population density of Minnesota. _____

7. Describe the population-density change that has taken place in the Los Angeles area from 1890 to the present. _____

_____

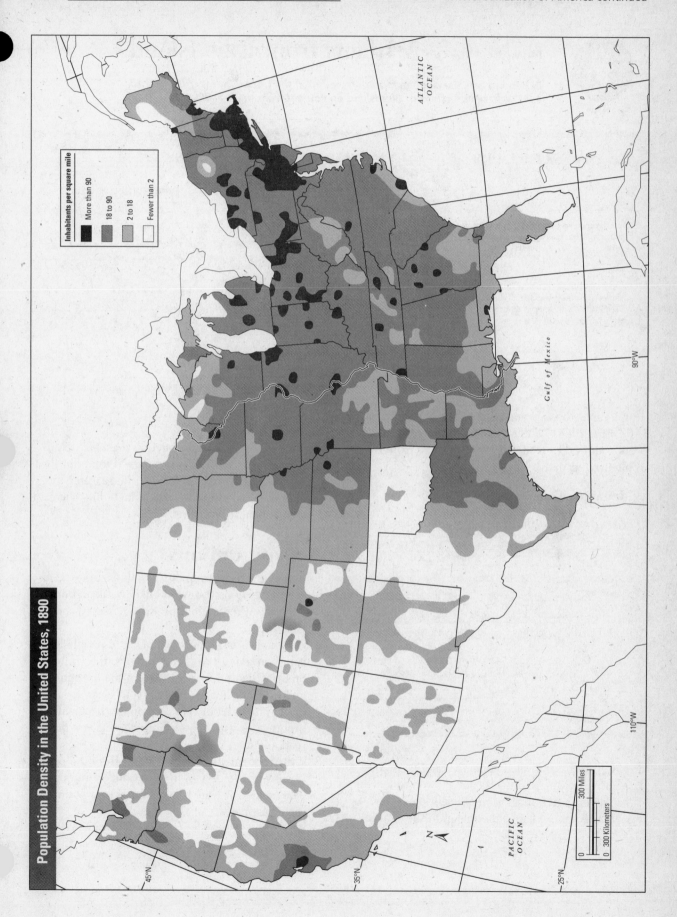

Population Density in the United States, 1890

Inhabitants per square mile

- More than 90
- 18 to 90
- 2 to 18
- Fewer than 2

ATLANTIC OCEAN

Gulf of Mexico

PACIFIC OCEAN

90°W

110°W

45°N

35°N

25°N

N

300 Miles

0   300 Kilometers

PRIMARY SOURCE Artifacts from Ellis Island

Ellis Island was the chief immigration station in the United States from 1892 to 1943. What impressions of Ellis Island do you get from these artifacts?

Literacy Test Card, 1919

| Class No. 3 | Serial Number | 5698 | Polish |

Bądźcie posłuszni przewodnikom swoim, i ulegajcie im; albowiem oni czuwają nad duszami waszemi, jako mający zdać sprawę, aby to z radością czynili, a nie wzdychając; bo dla was to niepożyteczne.

Obey them that have the rule over you, and submit your-selves: for they watch for your souls, as they that must give account, that they may do it with joy, and not with grief: for that is unprofitable for you.

(Hebrews 13:17)

Ellis Island Literacy card—Polish. By courtesy of the Ellis Island Immigration Museum.

Immigrants 16 years and older had to pass a litera-cy test in order to enter the United States. They were required to read a 40-word passage from the Bible in their native language.

Immigrant's Telegram, 1912

THE WESTERN UNION TELEGRAPH COMPANY
INCORPORATED
25,000 OFFICES IN AMERICA.   CABLE SERVICE TO ALL THE WORLD

THEO. N. VAIL, PRESIDENT.   BELVIDERE BROOKS, GENERAL MANAGER

| NUMBER 15 | SENT BY 03 | REC'D BY 7 | CHECK 9-43 Q |

RECEIVED AT _____ 191__
DATED   Hn Stoboken n g 11
To   N Goldfusz
164 Ludlow st

Arrived Steamer Noordam meet me Ellis Island immediately Freide Goldfusz

Ellis Island telegram. By courtesy of the Ellis Island Immigration Museum.

Freide Goldfusz traveled alone to America to join her husband Morris. She was not allowed to leave Ellis Island until immigration officials knew she was in safe hands. This is the telegram she sent to her relatives in New Jersey.

Detention Card, 1899

FORM 1508
United States Immigration Service
ELLIS ISLAND, NEW YORK HARBOR.
DETENTION CARD.
Name, Franc and Andreas Perlow
Vessel Sed Bretagne
Date, Oct 27, 189 M.
CAUSE OF DETENTION:
No ticket to Kansas
Registry Clerk.
JAN. FEB. MARCH. APRIL. MAY. JUNE. JULY. AUG. SEPT. OCT. NOV. DEC.

Ellis Island Detention card. National Archives.

Immigrants who failed inspection received deten-tion cards like this one and remained temporarily at Ellis Island. Inspectors recorded the reason why some immigrants were detained, including a lack of money or health problems.

Activity Options

1. Working with a group of classmates, draw up a list of questions you would like to ask an immi-grant like Freide Goldfusz who passed through Ellis Island.
2. With your class, brainstorm a list of people in your community who emigrated to the United States. Choose one person from the list and invite him or her to speak to your class about immigration. Afterwards, compare the speaker's experiences with those of immigrants you have read about.
3. Write a poem about immigration from the point of view of Freide Goldfusz or another immigrant who arrived at Ellis Island. Share your poem with classmates.

CHAPTER 7

Section 2

PRIMARY SOURCE *from How the Other Half Lives*
by Jacob Riis

Jacob Riis, a Danish immigrant, worked for 12 years on the Lower East Side as a police reporter for the New York Tribune. In 1890 he published How the Other Half Lives, a shocking glimpse of slum life. What sights, sounds, and smells does Riis include in this description of a New York tenement?

Be a little careful, please! The hall is dark and you might stumble over the children pitching pennies back there. Not that it would hurt them; kicks and cuffs are their daily diet. They have little else. Here where the hall turns and dives into utter darkness is a step, and another, another. A flight of stairs. You can feel your way, if you cannot see it. Close? Yes! What would you have? All the fresh air that ever enters these stairs comes from the hall door that is forever slamming, and from the windows of dark bedrooms that in turn receive from the stairs their sole supply of the elements God meant to be free, but man deals out with such niggardly hand. That was a woman filling her pail by the hydrant you just bumped against. The sinks are in the hallway, that all the tenants may have access—and all be poisoned alike by their summer stenches. Hear the pump squeak! It is the lullaby of tenement house babes. In summer, when a thousand thirsty throats pant for a cooling drink in this block, it is worked in vain. But the saloon, whose open door you passed in the hall, is always there. The smell of it has followed you up. Here is a door. Listen! That short hacking cough, that tiny, helpless wail—what do they mean? They mean that the soiled bow of white [a sign of a recent birth] you saw on the door downstairs will have another story to tell—Oh! a sadly familiar story—before the day is at an end. The child is dying with measles. With half a chance it might have lived; but it had none. That dark bedroom killed it.

"It was took all of a suddint," says the mother, smoothing the throbbing little body with trembling hands. There is no unkindness in the rough voice of the man in the jumper, who sits by the window grimly smoking a clay pipe, with the little life ebbing out in his sight, bitter as his words sound: "Hush, Mary! If we cannot keep the baby, need we complain—such as we?"

Such as we! What if the words ring in your ears as we grope our way up the stairs and down from floor to floor, listening to the sounds behind the closed doors—some of quarrelling, some of coarse songs, more of profanity. They are true. When the summer heats come with their suffering they have meaning more terrible than words can tell. Come over here. Step carefully over this baby—it is a baby, spite of its rags and dirt—under these iron bridges called fire escapes, but loaded down, despite the incessant watchfulness of the firemen, with broken household goods, with washtubs and barrels, over which no man could climb from a fire. This gap between dingy brick walls is the yard. That strip of smoke-colored sky up there is the heaven of these people. Do you wonder the name does not attract them to the churches? That baby's parents live in the rear tenement here. She is at least as clean as the steps we are now climbing. There are plenty of houses with half a hundred such in. The tenement is much like the one in front we just left, only fouler, closer, darker—we will not say more cheerless. The word is a mockery. A hundred thousand people lived in rear tenements in New York last year. Here is a room neater than the rest. The woman, a stout matron with hard lines of care in her face, is at the washtub. "I try to keep the childer clean," she says, apologetically, but with a hopeless glance around. The spice of hot soapsuds is added to the air already tainted with the smell of boiling cabbage, of rags and uncleanliness all about.

from Jacob Riis, *How the Other Half Lives: Studies Among the Tenements of New York* (Cambridge, Mass.: Harvard University Press, 1970), 32–34.

Discussion Questions

1. What urban problems discussed in your textbook does Riis touch upon in this passage?
2. How would you describe the effect of poverty on children?
3. List three sights, sounds, and smells that in your opinion Riis used most effectively to evoke the reality of slum life.

CHAPTER 7

Section 2

PRIMARY SOURCE *from* Twenty Years at Hull-House
by Jane Addams

*On September 18, 1889, social reformers Jane Addams and Ellen Gates Starr
moved into Hull-House, a dilapidated mansion in the midst of the Chicago slums.
As you read this excerpt, think about why they undertook this social experiment.*

In those early days we were often asked why we had come to live on Halsted Street when we could afford to live somewhere else. I remember one man who used to shake his head and say it was "the strangest thing he had met in his experience," but who was finally convinced that it was "not strange but natural." In time it came to seem natural to all of us that the Settlement should be there. If it is natural to feed the hungry and care for the sick, it is certainly natural to give pleasure to the young, comfort to the aged, and to minister to the deep-seated craving for social intercourse that all men feel. Whoever does it is rewarded by something which, if not gratitude, is at least spontaneous and vital and lacks that irksome sense of obligation with which a substantial benefit is too often acknowledged. . . .

From the first it seemed understood that we were ready to perform the humblest neighborhood services. We were asked to wash the newborn babies, and to prepare the dead for burial, to nurse the sick, and to "mind the children."

Occasionally these neighborly offices unexpectedly uncovered ugly human traits. For six weeks after an operation we kept in one of our three bedrooms a forlorn little baby who, because he was born with a cleft palate, was most unwelcome even to his mother, and we were horrified when he died of neglect a week after he was returned to his home; a little Italian bride of fifteen sought shelter with us one November evening, to escape her husband who had beaten her every night for a week when he returned home from work, because she had lost her wedding ring. . . .

We were also early impressed with the curious isolation of many of the immigrants; an Italian woman once expressed her pleasure in the red roses that she saw at one of our receptions in surprise that they had been "brought so fresh all the way from Italy." She would not believe for an instant that they had been grown in America. She said that she had lived in Chicago for six years and had never seen any roses, whereas in Italy she had seen them every summer in great profusion. During all that time, of course, the woman had lived within ten blocks of a florist's window; she had not been more than a five-cent car ride away from the public parks; but she had never dreamed of faring forth for herself, and no one had taken her. Her conception of America had been the untidy street in which she lived and had made her long struggle to adapt herself to American ways.

But in spite of some untoward experiences, we were constantly impressed with the uniform kindness and courtesy we received. Perhaps these first days laid the simple human foundations which are certainly essential for continuous living among the poor: first, genuine preference for residence in an industrial quarter to any other part of the city, because it is interesting and makes the human appeal; and second, the conviction, in the words of Canon Barnett [the founder of the first settlement house, Toynbee Hall, in London] that the things which make men alike are finer and better than the things that keep them apart, and that these basic likenesses, if they are properly accentuated, easily transcend the less essential differences of race, language, creed, and tradition.

Perhaps even in those first days we made a beginning toward that object which was afterwards stated in our charter: "To provide a center for a higher civic and social life; to institute and maintain educational and philanthropic enterprises; and to investigate and improve the conditions in the industrial districts of Chicago."

from Jane Addams, *Twenty Years at Hull-House* (Urbana: University of Illinois Press, 1990), 65–66.

Research Options

1. Use a print or on-line encyclopedia to find out more about the settlement-house movement, including Hull-House. Prepare an oral report.
2. Find out more about Jane Addams. Then write a brief author's note for a new edition of *Twenty Years at Hull-House.*

CHAPTER 7

Section 3

PRIMARY SOURCE *from The Shame of the Cities*
by Lincoln Steffens

Muckraking journalist Lincoln Steffens investigated political corruption in American cities. As you read this excerpt from his book, consider why he viewed Philadelphia as "a disgrace not to itself alone, nor to Pennsylvania, but to the United States."

The Philadelphia machine isn't the best. It isn't sound, and I doubt if it would stand in New York or Chicago. The enduring strength of the typical American political machine is that it is a natural growth—a sucker, but deep-rooted in the people. The New Yorkers vote for Tammany Hall. The Philadelphians do not vote; they are disenfranchised, and their disenfranchisement is one anchor of the foundation of the Philadelphia organization.

This is no figure of speech. The honest citizens of Philadelphia have no more rights at the polls than the Negroes down South. Nor do they fight very hard for this basic privilege. You can arouse their Republican ire by talking about the black Republican votes lost in the Southern States by white Democratic intimidation, but if you remind the average Philadelphian that he is in the same position, he will look startled, then say, "That's so, that's literally true, only I never thought of it in just that way." And it is literally true.

The machine controls the whole process of voting, and practices fraud at every stage. The assessor's list is the voting list, and the assessor is the machine's man. . . . The assessor pads the list with the names of dead dogs, children, and non-existent persons. One newspaper printed the picture of a dog, another that of a little four-year-old Negro boy, down on such a list. A ring orator in a speech resenting sneers at his ward as "low down" reminded his hearers that that was the ward of Independence Hall, and, naming the signers of the Declaration of Independence, he closed his highest flight of eloquence with the statement that "these men, the fathers of American liberty, voted down here once. And," he added, with a catching grin, "they vote here yet."

Rudolph Blankenburg, a persistent fighter for the right and the use of the right to vote (and, by the way, an immigrant), sent out just before one election a registered letter to each voter on the rolls of a certain selected division. Sixty-three per cent were returned marked "not at," "removed," "deceased," etc. From one four-story house where forty-four voters were addressed, eighteen letters came back undelivered; from another of forty-eight voters, came back forty-one letters; from another sixty-one out of sixty-two; from another forty-four out of forty-seven. Six houses in one division were assessed at one hundred and seventy-two voters, more than the votes cast in the previous election in any one of two hundred entire divisions.

The repeating is done boldly, for the machine controls the election officers, often choosing them from among the fraudulent names; and when no one appears to serve, assigning the heeler [local political party worker] ready for the expected vacancy. The police are forbidden by law to stand within thirty feet of the polls, but they are at the box and they are there to see that the machine's orders are obeyed and that repeaters whom they help to furnish are permitted to vote without "intimidation" on the names they, the police, have supplied.

The editor of an anti-machine paper who was looking about for himself once told me that a ward leader who knew him well asked him into a polling place. "I'll show you how it's done," he said, and he had the repeaters go round and round voting again and again on the names handed them on slips. "But," as the editor said, "that isn't the way it's done." The repeaters go from one polling place to another, voting on slips, and on their return rounds change coats, hats, etc.

from Lincoln Steffens, *The Shame of the Cities* (New York: 1904). Reprinted in Richard B. Morris and James Woodress, eds., *Voices From America's Past*, Vol. 2, *Backwoods Democracy to World Power* (New York: Dutton, 1963), 238–240.

Discussion Questions

1. How did Philadelphia's machine control voting?
2. Why did Steffens claim that Philadelphians do not vote?
3. Why do you think Philadelphia's political machine flourished in the late 19th century?

CHAPTER 7

Section 1

LITERATURE SELECTION *from* *Call It Sleep*
by Henry Roth

This novel tells the story of David Schearl, an immigrant boy who comes to the United States in the early 1900s and grows up in the dark, crowded tenements of New York. What happens when David and his mother first arrive at Ellis Island?

The small white steamer, *Peter Stuyvesant*, that delivered the immigrants from the stench and throb of the steerage to the stench and throb of New York tenements, rolled slightly on the water beside the stone quay in the lee of the weathered barracks and new brick buildings of Ellis Island. Her skipper was waiting for the last of the officials, laborers and guards to embark upon her before he cast off and started for Manhattan. Since this was Saturday afternoon and this the last trip she would make for the week-end, those left behind might have to stay over till Monday. Her whistle bellowed its hoarse warning. A few figures in overalls sauntered from the high doors of the immigration quarters and down the grey pavement that led to the dock.

It was May of the year 1907, the year that was destined to bring the greatest number of immigrants to the shores of the United States. All that day, as on all the days since spring began, her decks had been thronged by hundreds upon hundreds of foreigners, natives from almost every land in the world, the joweled close-cropped Teuton, the full-bearded Russian, the scraggly-whiskered Jew, and among them Slovack peasants with docile faces, smooth-cheeked and swarthy Armenians, pimply Greeks, Danes with wrinkled eyelids. All day her decks had been colorful, a matrix of the vivid costumes of other lands, the speckled green-and-yellow aprons, the flowered kerchief, embroidered homespun, the silver-braided sheepskin vest, the gaudy scarfs, yellow boots, fur caps, caftans, dull gabardines. All day the guttural, the high-pitched voices, the astonished cries, the gasps of wonder, reiterations of gladness had risen from her decks in a motley billow of sound. But now her decks were empty, quiet, spreading out under the sunlight almost as if the warm boards were relaxing from the strain and the

He paid only the scantest attention to the Statue of Liberty or to the city rising from the water or to the bridges spanning the East River.

pressure of the myriads of feet. All those steerage passengers of the ships that had docked that day who were permitted to enter had already entered—except two, a woman and a young child she carried in her arms. They had just come aboard escorted by a man.

About the appearance of these late comers there was very little that was unusual. The man had evidently spent some time in America and was now bringing his wife and child over from the other side. It might have been thought that he had spent most of his time in lower New York, for he paid only the scantest attention to the Statue of Liberty or to the city rising from the water or to the bridges spanning the East River—or perhaps he was merely too agitated to waste much time on these wonders. His clothes were the ordinary clothes the ordinary New Yorker wore in that period—sober and dull. A black derby accentuated the sharpness and sedentary pallor of his face; a jacket, loose on his tall spare frame, buttoned up in a V close to the throat; and above the V a tightly-knotted black tie was mounted in the groove of a high starched collar. As for his wife, one guessed that she was a European more by the timid wondering look in her eyes as she gazed from her husband to the harbor, than by her clothes. For her clothes were American—a black skirt, a white shirt-waist and a black jacket. Obviously her husband had either taken the precaution of sending them to her while she was still in Europe or had brought them with him to Ellis Island where she had slipped them on before she left.

Only the small child in her arms wore a distinctly foreign costume, an impression one got chiefly from the odd, outlandish, blue straw hat on his head with its polka dot ribbons of the same color dangling over each shoulder.

Except for this hat, had the three newcomers been in a crowd, no one probably could have singled out the woman and child as newly arrived immigrants. They carried no sheets tied up in huge bundles, no bulky wicker baskets, no prized feather beds, no boxes of delicacies, sausages, virgin-olive oils, rare cheeses; the large black satchel beside them was their only luggage. But despite this, despite their even less than commonplace appearance, the two overalled men, sprawled out and smoking cigarettes in the stern, eyed them curiously. And the old peddler woman, sitting with basket of oranges on knee, continually squinted her weak eyes in their direction.

The truth was there was something quite untypical about their behavior. The old peddler woman on the bench and the overalled men in the stern had seen enough husbands meeting their wives and children after a long absence to know how such people ought to behave. The most volatile races, such as the Italians, often danced for joy, whirled each other around, pirouetted in an ecstasy; Swedes sometimes just looked at each other, breathing through open mouths like a panting dog; Jews wept, jabbered, almost put each other's eyes out with the recklessness of their darting gestures; Poles roared and gripped each other at arm's length as though they meant to tear a handful of flesh; and after one pecking kiss, the English might be seen gravitating toward, but never achieving an embrace. But these two stood silent, apart; the man staring with aloof, offended eyes grimly down at the water—or if he turned his face toward his wife at all, it was only to glare in harsh contempt at the blue straw hat worn by the child in her arms, and then his hostile eyes would sweep about the deck to see if anyone else were observing them. And his wife beside him regarding him uneasily, appealingly. And the child against her breast looking from one to the other with watchful, frightened eyes. Altogether it was a very curious meeting.

They had been standing in this strange and silent manner for several minutes, when the woman, as if driven by the strain into action, tried to smile, and touching her husband's arm said timidly, "And this is the Golden Land." She spoke in Yiddish.

The man grunted, but made no answer.

She took a breath as if taking courage, and tremu-

lously, "I'm sorry, Albert, I was so stupid." She paused waiting for some flicker of unbending, some word, which never came. "But you look so lean, Albert, so haggard. And your mustache—you've shaved."

His brusque glance stabbed and withdrew. "Even so."

"You must have suffered in this land." She continued gentle despite his rebuke. "You never wrote me. You're thin. Ach! Then here in the new land is the same old poverty. You've gone without food. I can see it. You've changed."

"Well that don't matter," he snapped, ignoring her sympathy. "It's no excuse for your not recognizing me. Who else would call for you? Do you know anyone else in this land?"

"No," placatingly. "But I was so frightened, Albert. Listen to me. I was so bewildered, and that long waiting there in that vast room since morning. Oh, that horrible waiting! I saw them all go, one after the other. The shoemaker and his wife. The coppersmith and his children from Strij. All those on the Kaiserin Viktoria. But I—I remained. To-morrow will be Sunday. They told me no one could come to fetch me. What if they sent me back? I was frantic!"

"They didn't have any more third-class passage, so I had to take the steerage—"

"Are you blaming me?" His voice was dangerous.

"No! No! Of course not Albert! I was just explaining."

"Well then let me explain," he said curtly. "I did what I could. I took the day off from the shop. I called that cursed Hamburg-American Line four times. And each time they told me you weren't on board."

"They didn't have any more third-class passage, so I had to take the steerage—"

"Yes, now I know. That's all very well. That couldn't be helped. I came here anyway. The last boat. And what do you do? You refused to recognize me. You don't know me." He dropped his elbows down on the rail, averted his angry face. "That's the greeting I get."

"I'm sorry, Albert," she stroked his arm humbly. "I'm sorry."

"And as if those blue-coated mongrels in there weren't mocking me enough, you give them that brat's right age. Didn't I write you to say seventeen months because it would save half fare! Didn't you hear me inside when I told them?"

"How could I, Albert?" she protested. "How could I? You were on the other side of that—that cage."

"Well why didn't you say seventeen months anyway? Look!" he pointed to several blue-coated officials who came hurrying out of a doorway out of the immigration quarters. "There they are." An ominous pride dragged at his voice. "If he's among them, that one who questioned so much, I could speak to him if he came up here."

"Don't bother with him, Albert," she exclaimed uneasily. "Please, Albert! What have you against him? He couldn't help it. It's his work."

"Is it?" His eyes followed with unswerving deliberation the blue-coats as they neared the boat. "Well he didn't have to do it so well."

"And after all, I did lie to him, Albert," she said hurriedly trying to distract him.

"The truth is you didn't," he snapped, turning his anger against her. "You made your first lie plain by telling the truth afterward. And made a laughing-stock of me!"

"I didn't know what to do." She picked despairingly at the wire grill beneath the rail. "In Hamburg the doctor laughed at me when I said seventeen months. He's so big. He was big when he was born." She smiled, the worried look on her face vanishing momentarily as she stroked her son's cheek. "Won't you speak to your father, David, beloved?"

The child merely ducked his head behind his mother.

His father stared at him, shifted his gaze and glared down at the officials, and then, as though perplexity had crossed his mind, he frowned absently. "How old did he say he was?"

"The doctor? Over two years—and as I say he laughed."

"Well what did he enter?"

"Seventeen months—I told you."

"Then why didn't you tell them seventeen—" He broke off, shrugged violently. "Baah! You need more strength in this land." He paused, eyed her intently and then frowned suddenly. "Did you bring his birth certificate?"

"Why—" She seemed confused. "It may be in the trunk—there on the ship. I don't know. Perhaps I left it behind." Her hand wandered uncertainly to her lips. "I don't know. Is it important? I never thought of it. But surely father could send it. We need only write."

"Hmm! Well, put him down." His head jerked brusquely toward the child. "You don't need to carry him all the way. He's big enough to stand on his own feet."

She hesitated, and then reluctantly set the child down on the deck. Scared, unsteady, the little one edged over to the side opposite his father, and hidden by his mother, clung to her skirt.

"Well, it's all over now." She attempted to be cheerful. "It's all behind us now, isn't it, Albert? Whatever mistakes I made don't really matter any more. Do they?"

"A fine taste of what lies before me!" He turned his back on her and leaned morosely against the rail. "A fine taste!"

They were silent. On the dock below, the brown hawsers had been slipped over the mooring posts, and the men on the lower deck now dragged them dripping from the water. Bells clanged. The ship throbbed. Startled by the hoarse bellow of her whistle, the gulls wheeling before her prow rose with slight creaking cry from the green water, and as she churned away from the stone quay skimmed across her path on indolent, scimitar wing. Behind the ship the white wake that stretched to Ellis Island grew longer, raveling wanly into melon-green. On one side curved the low drab Jersey coast-line, the spars and masts on the waterfront fringing the sky; on the other side was Brooklyn, flat, water-towered; the horns of the harbor. And before them, rising on her high pedestal from the scaling swarmy brilliance of sunlit water to the west, Liberty. The spinning disk of the late afternoon sun slanted behind her, and to those on board who gazed, her features were charred with shadow, her depths exhausted, her masses ironed to one single plane. Against the luminous sky the rays of her halo were spikes of darkness roweling the air; shadow flattened the torch she bore to a black cross against flawless light—the blackened hill of a broken sword. Liberty. The child and his mother stared again at the massive figure in wonder.

Activity Options

1. Draw a sketch to accompany this excerpt from *Call It Sleep*. Then display your sketch on a classroom bulletin board.
2. With a partner, role-play the Schearls' reunion on the docks of the *Peter Stuyvesant* for the class. Then discuss why you think Mr. and Mrs. Schearl react as they do.
3. Imagine that you are Mrs. Schearl. Write a postcard to a friend or family member back home in Poland in which you describe your trip to America.

CHAPTER 7

Section 2

AMERICAN LIVES Jane Addams
Helping the Poor—and the Well-to-Do

"Insanitary housing, poisonous sewage, contaminated water, infant mortality, the spread of contagion, adulterated food, impure milk, smoke-laden air, ill-ventilated factories, dangerous occupations, juvenile crime, unwholesome crowding, prostitution, and drunkenness are the enemies which the modern city must face and overcome would it survive."— Jane Addams, "Utilization of Women in City Government" (1907)

Jane Addams (1860–1935) dedicated herself to helping the many poor U.S. immigrants at the turn of the century. In the process of helping them, she also aimed to help even the middle class.

Illinois-born Jane Addams was little more than two when her mother died, and she was raised by her father. He was a successful businessman, and she loved him deeply. She attended college— unusual for females of her time—but the same year that she graduated, her father died. Plagued by frail health and dissatisfied with the restrictions of her middle-class life, Addams drifted for a few years. Then, on a tour of Europe with her college roommate, Ellen Gates Starr, she visited a settlement house in London. At Addams's urging, the two decided to create such a house in the United States.

They returned to the United States and in 1889 purchased a rundown mansion in Chicago. Hull House, as it was called, had been in the suburbs of Chicago when it was built. Now it was surrounded by tenements housing immigrants. It was the perfect location for their idea.

Addams and Starr did not know exactly what to do at first. One of their first programs offered the nearby Italian immigrants a chance to hear a novel read aloud in Italian and see photographs of Italy. The event was not a success. Soon, though, they saw a need: to create a kindergarten for the immigrants' young children. It was welcomed eagerly and launched many years of helpful programs. Eventually Hull House provided art and craft classes, created a theater group, and offered classes teaching English and job skills. The settlement house grew to be a large complex of buildings visited by some two thousand Chicagoans each week.

From the start, Hull House had two purposes. It was intended not only to help the poor immigrants but also to provide benefits for the middle class. Addams and Starr wished to give privileged young people—especially young women—a chance

to learn skills, experience life, and take part in important activity. By working at the settlement house, they could avoid "being cultivated into unnourished and over-sensitive lives."

They attracted many talented people to their work. Those who worked at Hull House backed such causes as improving urban sanitation and ending child labor. They convinced Illinois to require safety inspections in factories and to create the first court system for juveniles.

While Addams and Starr worked together at Hull House, Addams was the chief spokeswoman for the effort. In countless speeches and articles and a number of books, she backed various social reforms. She also became a powerful voice on behalf of opportunities for women.

In later years, she embraced the cause of peace. This position cost her some support during World War I, but she did not hesitate to take her stand. She became president of the Woman's International League for Peace and Freedom in 1919 and was a founding member of the American Civil Liberties Union the next year. For her peace efforts, she won the Nobel Peace Prize in 1931. She died just four years later.

Questions

1. What kind of programs do you think helped immigrants the most?
2. What opportunities were available to middle-class women in Addams's time?
3. Would it be helpful to have settlement houses or similar programs in cities today?

AMERICAN LIVES William Marcy "Boss" Tweed
Corrupt Boss of the Political Machine

"There is not in the history of villainy a parallel for the gigantic crime against property conspired [to] by the Tammany Ring."—Henry G. Stebbins, report of the Committee of Seventy that investigated the Tweed Ring (1871)

William Marcy Tweed was the most spectacular example of the corrupt boss of the urban political machine of the 1800s. Rising from obscurity to control New York City in a time of its great growth, Tweed and his friends raked in a fortune. Then their empire quickly collapsed.

Tweed (1823–1878) was born in New York. He became a bookkeeper and seemed ready for modest success. After becoming chief of a volunteer fire company, he turned to politics, running for alderman as a Democrat. Knowing that he would probably lose the election to the Whig candidate, he persuaded a friend to run as an independent Whig. By splitting that party's vote, Tweed won the election.

Tweed took over New York's Democratic Party, called Tammany Hall after its headquarters. Soon he was elected to the board of supervisors. Despite having no legal training, he opened a law office in 1860. One client paid him $100,000 in one year alone, knowing that his so-called legal advice would prove useful. Winning the election of friends to various city posts, "Boss" Tweed built his power. In 1861 his candidate defeated a rival for mayor. The campaign cost Tweed $100,000—but he made the money back quickly.

Soon thereafter Tweed was the head of several New York politicians, a corrupt group—known as a "ring"—that took over control of city finances. They cheated the government out of millions of dollars.

In 1868, the ring controlled the mayor of New York City, the speaker of the state assembly, and the state's governor. In 1869, the ring decided that all bills sent to New York City and the county would be doubled, with the extra money going into their pockets. Later the share was increased even more. Because the city did not enjoy complete freedom from state control, Tweed had a new city charter written. It appeared to simplify city government, thus winning the support of many prominent New Yorkers as a useful reform. Its real purpose, though, was to increase Tammany control over the city government. Tweed got the state legislature to pass the charter.

By authorizing the building of the Brooklyn Bridge, Tweed collected $40,000 in stock. The millions received from the fraudulent scheme to build the county courthouse was split five ways. Four parts went to Tweed and three friends. The final share was used to distribute among lesser politicians.

In 1870, the press began a campaign against the Tweed Ring. *Harper's Weekly*, led by cartoonist Thomas Nast, was first. It was followed by the *New York Times*. The next year, two Democratic opponents of the ring gave the *Times* official records that showed widespread corruption. The ring offered the newspaper $5 million not to publish the evidence—and another $500,000 to Nast to stop drawing his cartoons. But they went ahead, and New Yorkers rose in anger. An investigating committee condemned Tweed and his partners, who were then arrested. Tweed spent his last eight years in and out of court and prison. He died in jail at age 55.

Questions

1. What was Tweed's first political "dirty trick"?
2. What was the secret to Tweed's success as long as it lasted?
3. The evidence offered to the *New York Times* in 1871 included pages from the city's account books. Why would they be damaging to the ring?

Name _____ Date _____

CHAPTER
8
Section 1

GUIDED READING *Science and Urban Life*

A. As you read about how technological changes at the turn of the 20th century affected American life, write notes in the appropriate boxes. Leave the shaded boxes blank.

	1. Who was involved in its development?	2. What other inventions helped make this one possible?	3. How did this invention or development affect Americans' lives?
Skyscraper			
Electric transit			
Suspension bridge			
Urban planning			
Airmail			
Web-perfecting press			
Kodak camera			

B. On the back of this paper, explain how **Central Park** can be considered an achievement in science.

Name _____ Date _____

GUIDED READING *Expanding Public Education*

A. As you read this section, write notes to describe the chief characteristics of each type of educational institution and the developments that took place at the turn of the 20th century.

	Chief Characteristics and Important Developments
1. Elementary schools	
2. High schools	
3. Colleges and universities	
4. Education for immigrant adults	

B. On the back of this paper, briefly describe the contribution of each of the following people to American education during this time.

W. E. B. Du Bois   **Booker T. Washington**   **Henry Ford**

CHAPTER 8
Section 3

GUIDED READING *Segregation and Discrimination*

A. As you read about racial tensions at the turn of the 20th century, write notes to answer the questions.

	In what region or regions did it exist?	Who were its targets?	How did it affect the lives of these people?
1. Literacy test			
2. Poll tax			
3. Grandfather clause			
4. Jim Crow laws			
5. Racial etiquette			
6. Debt peonage			
7. Chinese Exclusion Act			

B. On the back of this paper, explain why **Ida B. Wells** is a significant historical figure and note what the Supreme Court said about **segregation** in *Plessy v. Ferguson.*

Name _____ Date _____

GUIDED READING *The Dawn of Mass Culture*

A. As you read about the emergence of modern mass culture, give *either* an example of each item *or* mention one of the people who invented or popularized it. Then note one reason why the item became so popular around the turn of the 20th century.

	1. Amusement parks	2. Bicycling	3. Boxing	4. Baseball
Example				
Reason				

	5. Shopping centers	6. Department stores	7. Chain stores	8. Mail-order catalogs
Example				
Reason				

B. On the back of this paper, describe the impact that **rural free delivery** had on the country.

Name _____ Date _____

BUILDING VOCABULARY *Life at the Turn of the 20th Century*

A. Matching Match the characterization in the second column with the correct person in the first column. Write the appropriate letter next to the word.

_____ 1. Wright Brothers   a. fought to end lynching

_____ 2. W. E. B. Du Bois   b. introduced first mass-produced camera

_____ 3. Joseph Pulitzer   c. American novelist and humorist

_____ 4. Louis Sullivan   d. originated planned urban parks

_____ 5. George Eastman   e. developed first airplane

_____ 6. Frederick Law Olmsted   f. designed nation's first skyscraper

_____ 7. Mark Twain   g. demanded immediate equality for blacks

_____ 8. Ida B. Wells   h. pioneered several newspaper innovations

B. Completion Select the term or name that best completes the sentence.

Niagra Movement	poll tax	William Randolph Hearst
Daniel Burnham	grandfather clause	debt peonage
Ashcan School	rural free delivery	Booker T. Washington

1. _____ encouraged African Americans to fight racism by proving their economic value to society.

2. The _____ was an effort to encourage blacks to seek a liberal arts education in order to provide the African American community with well-educated leaders.

3. The _____, or an annual tax that had to be paid in order to vote, was an effort to discourage African Americans from voting.

4. The owner of the New York Morning Journal, _____ sought to lure readers with exaggerated stories.

5. Introduced by the Post Office in 1896, the _____ system brought packages directly to every home.

C. Writing Write a paragraph describing the plight of African Americans at the turn of the century using the following terms.

Jim Crow laws   segregation   *Plessy* v. *Ferguson*

CHAPTER
8
Section 3

SKILLBUILDER PRACTICE *Creating Visual Presentations*

Use the chart below to list four types of visuals you could use–and how you would use them–to create a visual presentation on the discrimination and segregation that the nation's minority groups endured during the turn of the 20th century. (See Skillbuilder Handbook, p. R37.)

Visual	Purpose

Name _____ Date _____

CHAPTER
8
Section 1

RETEACHING ACTIVITY *Science and Urban Life*

Evaluating

A. Write *T* in the blank if the statement is true. If the statement is false, write *F* in the blank and then write the corrected statement on the line below.

_____ 1. By the turn of the twentieth century about nine out of ten Americans made their homes in cities.

_____

_____ 2. "Make no little plans. They have no magic to stir man's blood" was the motto of urban designer Daniel Burnham.

_____

_____ 3. The first successful flight took place in Omaha, Nebraska.

_____

_____ 4. The "Emerald Necklace" refers to the city of Chicago's park system.

_____

_____ 5. The development of an easy-to-use camera helped to develop the field of photojournalism.

_____

Summarizing

B. On the line next to each person list the field in which they made a notable achievement.

_____ 1. Louis Sullivan

_____ 2. Frederick Law Olmsted

_____ 3. Daniel Burnham

_____ 4. Orville and Wilbur Wright

_____ 5. George Eastman

RETEACHING ACTIVITY *Expanding Public Education*

Finding Main Ideas

The following questions deal with reforms in public education. Answer them in the space provided.

1. Why did education become more important during the industrial age?

_____

_____

2. Why were many immigrants encouraged to go to school?

_____

_____

3. How did the nation's high schools change during the late 1800s and early 1900s?

_____

_____

4. How did college curricula change during the turn of the century?

_____

_____

5. How did African Americans pursue higher education despite their exclusion
   from white institutions?

_____

_____

6. How did Booker T. Washington and W. E. B. Du Bois differ in their views on
   education for African Americans?

_____

_____

Name _____ Date _____

CHAPTER

8

Section 3

RETEACHING ACTIVITY *Segregation and Discrimination*

Analyzing

A. Complete the chart shown here by describing how each of the entries kept African Americans from attaining full civil rights

Measure	Effect
Poll Tax	
Jim Crow laws	
Plessy v. *Ferguson*	

Completion

B. Select the term or name that best completes the sentence.

African Americans   grandfather clause   racial discrimination
Sixteenth Amendment   Thirteenth Amendment   Mexicans

1. _____ existed in the North as well as the South, as many Northern cities were segregated.

2. By the late 1800s, _____ made up the largest ethnic group of railroad workers in the Southwest.

3. In 1911, the Supreme Court declared the system of debt peonage a violation of the _____.

4. The _____ was intended to allow poor whites to circumvent the poll tax.

Name _____ Date _____

Reading Comprehension

Choose the best answer for each item. Write the letter of your answer in the blank.

_____ 1. The sport that the novelist Mark Twain referred to as the symbol of the "booming nineteenth century" was
   a. football.
   b. baseball.
   c. soccer.
   d. boxing.

_____ 2. Dime novels were inexpensive books that often told glorified adventure tales of
   a. the sea.
   b. the West.
   c. escaped slaves.
   d. the business world.

_____ 3. The man who originated the department store was
   a. Stephen Crane.
   b. F. W. Woolworth.
   c. Thomas Eakins.
   d. Marshall Field.

_____ 4. By 1910, the number of Americans who shopped by mail had reached
   a. 5 million.
   b. 10 million.
   c. 15 million.
   d. 20 million.

_____ 5. The popular Ashcan School of American art stressed scenes of
   a. nature.
   b. Southern living.
   c. urban life.
   d. the wealthy and elite.

_____ 6. The activity that the suffragist Susan B. Anthony said "has done more to emancipate women than anything else in the world" was
   a. bicycling.
   b. baseball.
   c. shopping.
   d. tennis.

Name _____ Date _____

GEOGRAPHY APPLICATION: HUMAN–ENVIRONMENT INTERACTION

New York's Central Park

Directions: Read the paragraphs below and study the drawings and map carefully. Then answer the questions that follow.

During the 1800s, Frederick Law Olmsted pioneered the use of natural landscaping in urban parks. He designed more than 80 public parks in Boston, Chicago, and other cities. In addition, Olmsted designed the grounds around the Capitol building in Washington, D.C.

Olmsted's lasting contribution, though, was the setting aside of natural areas in crowded cities. These areas gave urban residents places for recreation. To Olmsted, recreation meant walking in a pleasant environment. As he once said:

The main object and justification [of the park] is simply to produce a certain influence in the minds of people, and through this to make life in the city healthier and happier. The character of this influence is a poetic one and it is to be produced by means of scenes.

In 1858, Olmsted and the architect Calvert Vaux won a prize for their design of Central Park, an 843-acre oblong area in the center of Manhattan in New York City. Their design was unique for city parks in the United States. Rural scenery was the theme of the design. A screen of trees and shrubs around the park blocked the city from view. Traffic was routed through underground passes. A few small lakes were created. Avenues for carriages, bridle paths for horses, and an elaborate system of footpaths laced the park grounds. Central Park today remains an oasis amid concrete sprawl.

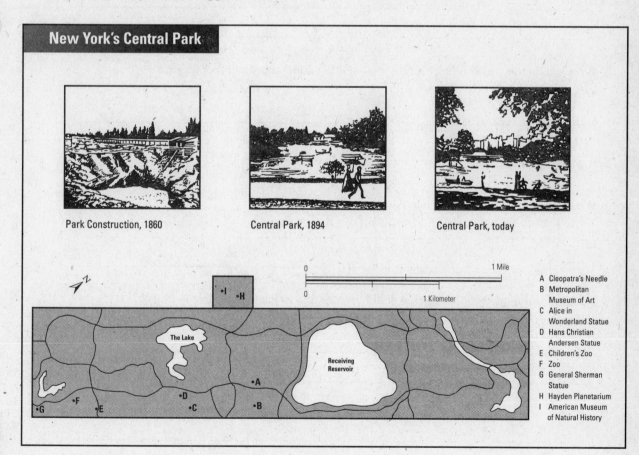

New York's Central Park

Park Construction, 1860

Central Park, 1894

Central Park, today

A Cleopatra's Needle
B Metropolitan Museum of Art
C Alice in Wonderland Statue
D Hans Christian Andersen Statue
E Children's Zoo
F Zoo
G General Sherman Statue
H Hayden Planetarium
I American Museum of Natural History

The Lake

Receiving Reservoir

0 ——————— 1 Mile
0 ——————— 1 Kilometer

Interpreting Text and Visuals

1. What did Olmsted believe was the purpose of parks? _____

_____

_____

2. Why do you think Olmsted is called the father of urban planning? _____

_____

3. Using the pictures and text for reference, describe what was done to create
   the Central Park of today.

_____

_____

_____

4. Categorize the types of attractions found in the park. _____

_____

_____

5. What are the dimensions of Central Park—not including the small section with
   locations H and I?

_____

6. A person walking from locations D to A moves in what direction? _____

7. What legacy has Olmsted given to Americans? _____

_____

_____

8. What do you think is one thing that could be added to or taken away from
   Olmsted's Central Park plan that would improve the park?

_____

_____

_____

_____

CHAPTER 8

Section 1

PRIMARY SOURCE *from* Orville Wright's Diary

On December 17, 1903, Orville and Wilbur Wright made the first airplane flight at Kitty Hawk, North Carolina. As you read this excerpt from Orville's diary, think about the challenges as well as the historical significance of this event.

When we got up, a wind of between 20 and 25 miles was blowing from the north. We got the machine out early and put out the signal for the men at the station. Before we were quite ready, John T. Daniels, W. S. Dough, A. D. Etheridge, W. C. Brinkley of Manteo, and Johnny Moore of Nag's Head arrived. After running the engine and propellers a few minutes to get them in working order, I got on the machine at 10:35 for the first trial. The wind according to our anemometer [instrument for indicating and measuring wind force and velocity] at this time was blowing a little over 20 miles (corrected) 27 miles according to the Government anemometer at Kitty Hawk. On slipping the rope the machine started off increasing in speed to probably 7 or 8 miles. The machine lifted from the truck just as it was entering on the fourth rail. Mr. Daniels took a picture just as it left the trucks. [The trucks were a primitive sort of wheel assembly, which enabled the plane to take off along a track made from two-by-fours. When the plane took off, it left the truck on the ground and hence flew without any landing gear.]

I found the control of the front rudder quite difficult on account of its being balanced too near the center and thus had a tendency to turn itself when started so that the rudder was turned too far on one side and then too far on the other. As a result the machine would rise suddenly to about 10 feet and then as suddenly, on turning the rudder, dart for the ground. A sudden dart when out about 100 feet from the end of the track ended the flight. Time about 12 seconds (not known exactly as watch was not promptly stopped). The flight lever for throwing off the engine was broken, and the skid under the rudder cracked.

After repairs, at 20 minutes after 11 o'clock Will [Orville's brother Wilbur] made the second trial. The course was about like mine, up and down but a little longer . . . over the ground though about the same in time. Distance not measured but about 175 feet. Wind speed not quite so strong.

With the aid of the station men present, we picked the machine up and carried it back to the starting ways. At about 20 minutes till 12 o'clock I

made the third trial. When out about the same distance as Will's, I met with a strong gust from the left which raised the left wing and sidled the machine off to the right in a lively manner. I immediately turned the rudder to bring the machine down and then worked the end control. Much to our surprise, on reaching the ground the left wing struck first, showing the lateral control of this machine much more effective than on any of our former ones. At the time of its sidling it had raised to a height of probably 12 to 14 feet.

At just 12 o'clock Will started on the fourth and last trip. The machine started off with its ups and downs as it had before, but by the time he had gone three or four hundred feet he had it under much better control, and was traveling on a fairly even course. It proceeded in this manner till it reached a small hummock out about 800 feet from the starting ways, when it began its pitching again and suddenly darted into the ground. The front rudder frame was badly broken up, but the main frame suffered none at all. The distance over the ground was 852 feet in 59 seconds. . . .

After removing the front rudder, we carried the machine back to camp. We set the machine down a few feet west of the building, and while standing about discussing the last flight, a sudden gust of wind struck the machine and started to turn it over. All rushed to stop it. Will, who was near the end, ran to the front, but too late to do any good. Mr. Daniels and myself seized spars at the rear, but to no purpose. The machine gradually turned over on us.

from Richard B. Morris and James Woodress, eds., *Voices from America's Past*, Vol. 2, *Backwoods Democracy to World Power* (New York: Dutton, 1963), 293–295.

Discussion Questions

1. How many trial runs did the Wright brothers make on December 17?
2. What was the longest powered flight the Wright brothers made on this day?
3. What kinds of difficulties did the Wright brothers encounter during these trials?

CHAPTER 8

Section 1

PRIMARY SOURCE *Advertisement*

George Eastman invented the Kodak camera in 1888. After a photographer snapped a roll of film, he or she shipped the film for processing—and the camera for reloading—to the Eastman factory. To learn more about the Kodak camera and its features, examine this early advertisement.

The Kodak Camera

" You press the button, we do the rest."

OR YOU CAN DO IT YOURSELF.

The only camera that anybody can use without instructions. As convenient to carry as an ordinary field glass World-wide success.

The Kodak is for sale by all Photo stock dealers.
Send for the Primer, free.

The Eastman Dry Plate & Film Co.

Price, $25.00 — Loaded for 100 Pictures.   **ROCHESTER, N. Y.**
Re-loading, $2.00.

Corbis-Bettmann

Activity Options

1. Find camera ads in an advertising circular or a current newspaper or magazine. Then make a Venn diagram in which you compare and contrast the features and prices of today's cameras with those of this Kodak camera.

2. Imagine you are an amateur photographer in the early 1900s. Write a letter to George Eastman in which you express your opinion of his Kodak camera.

3. Using this ad as a model, design your own ad for an early Kodak camera. Before you begin, refer to your textbook (page 281) for additional information.

Name _____   Date _____

CHAPTER
8

Section 2

PRIMARY SOURCE *from* "The Talented Tenth"
by W. E. B. Du Bois

W. E. B. Du Bois believed that the educated African Americans of his day—the "Talented Tenth"—would save the race by setting an example to whites and uplifting other African Americans. As you read this excerpt from Du Bois's essay, think about whether you agree or disagree with the theory that he puts forth.

The Negro race, like all races, is going to be saved by its exceptional men. The problem of education, then, among Negroes must first of all deal with the Talented Tenth; it is the problem of developing the Best of this race that they may guide the Mass away from the contamination and death of the Worst, in their own and other races. Now the training of men is a difficult and intricate task. Its technique is a matter for educational experts, but its object is for the vision of seers. If we make money the object of man-training, we shall develop money-makers but not necessarily men; if we make technical skill the object of education, we may possess artisans but not, in nature, men. Men we shall have only as we make manhood the object of the work of the schools—intelligence, broad sympathy, knowledge of the world that was and is, and of the relation of men to it—this is the curriculum of that Higher Education which must underlie true life. On this foundation we may build bread winning, skill of hand and quickness of brain, with never a fear lest the child and man mistake the means of living for the object of life. . . .

Can the masses of the Negro people be in any possible way more quickly raised than by the effort and example of this aristocracy of talent and character? Was there ever a nation on God's fair earth civilized from the bottom upward? Never; it is, ever was and ever will be from the top downward that culture filters. The Talented Tenth rises and pulls all that are worth the saving up to their vantage ground. This is the history of human progress; and the two historic mistakes which have hindered that progress were the thinking first that no more could ever rise save the few already risen; or second, that it would better the unrisen to pull the risen down.

How then shall the leaders of a struggling people be trained and the hands of the risen few strengthened? There can be but one answer: The best and most capable of their youth must be schooled in the colleges and universities of the land. We will not quarrel as to just what the

university of the Negro should teach or how it should teach it—I willingly admit that each soul and each race-soul needs its own peculiar curriculum. But this is true: A university is a human invention for the transmission of knowledge and culture from generation to generation, through the training of quick minds and pure hearts, and for this work no other human invention will suffice, not even trade and industrial schools. . . .

Men of America, the problem is plain before you. Here is a race transplanted through the criminal foolishness of your fathers. Whether you like it or not the millions are here, and here they will remain. If you do not lift them up, they will pull you down. Education and work are the levers to uplift a people. Work alone will not do it unless inspired by the right ideals and guided by intelligence. Education must not simply teach work—it must teach Life. The Talented Tenth of the Negro race must be made leaders of thought and missionaries of culture among their people. No others can do this work and Negro colleges must train men for it. The Negro race, like all other races, is going to be saved by its exceptional men.

from W. E. B. Du Bois, "The Talented Tenth," in *The Negro Problem: A Series of Articles by Representative American Negroes of Today* (New York: James Pott, 1903), 33–75.

Research Options

1. Imagine that you have been asked to introduce a speaker at an education conference: Dr. W. E. B. Du Bois. Find out more about Du Bois and then write a brief introduction based on your findings.
2. Du Bois believed education was a lever "to uplift a people." Find recent statistics about the number of African-American college graduates. Then compare these figures with the number of African-American college graduates—3,880—in 1900.

CHAPTER
8

Section 3

PRIMARY SOURCE *from* "Lynching and the Excuse for It" by Ida B. Wells

Ida B. Wells crusaded against lynching throughout the United States and Europe. In this article, which she published in the magazine Independent *in 1901, she attacks the assumption that lynching resulted from a desire for justice. As you read, consider the conclusion she draws about the cause of lynching.*

It was eminently befitting that the *Independent's* first number in the new century should contain a strong protest against lynching. The deepest dyed infamy of the 19th century was that which, in its supreme contempt for law, defied all constitutional guarantees of citizenship, and during the last fifteen years of the century put to death 2,000 men, women, and children by shooting, hanging, and burning alive. Well would it have been if every preacher in every pulpit in the land had made so earnest a plea as that which came from Miss Addams' forceful pen.

Appreciating the helpful influences of such a dispassionate and logical argument as that made by the writer referred to, I earnestly desire to say nothing to lessen the force of the appeal. At the same time, an unfortunate presumption used as a basis for her argument works so serious, though doubtless unintentional, an injury to the memory of thousands of victims of mob law that it is only fair to call attention to this phase of the writer's plea. It is unspeakably infamous to put thousands of people to death without a trial by jury; it adds to that infamy to charge that these victims were moral monsters, when, in fact, four-fifths of them were not so accused even by the fiends who murdered them.

Almost at the beginning of her discussion the distinguished writer says: "Let us assume that the Southern citizens who take part in and abet the lynching of Negroes honestly believe that that is the only successful method of dealing with a certain class of crimes."

It is this assumption, this absolutely unwarrantable assumption, that vitiates every suggestion which it inspires Miss Addams to make. It is the same baseless assumption which influences ninety-nine out of every one hundred persons who discuss this question. Among many thousand editorial clippings I have received in the past five years 99 percent discuss the question upon the presumption that lynchings are the desperate effort of the Southern people to protect their women from black

monsters, and, while the large majority condemn lynching, the condemnation is tempered with a plea for the lyncher—that human nature gives way under such awful provocation and that the mob, insane for the moment, must be pitied as well as condemned. It is strange that an intelligent, law-abiding, and fair-minded people should so persistently shut their eyes to the facts in the discussion of what the civilized world now concedes to be America's national crime.

This almost universal tendency to accept as true the slander which the lynchers offer to civilization as an excuse for their crime might be explained if the true facts were difficult to obtain; but not the slightest difficulty intervenes. The Associated Press dispatches, the press clipping bureau, frequent book publications, and the annual summary of a number of influential journals give the lynching record every year. . . .

A careful classification of the offenses which have caused lynchings during the past five years shows that contempt for law and race prejudice constitute the real cause of all lynching. During the past five years, 147 white persons were lynched. It may be argued that fear of the "law's delays" was the cause of their being lynched. But this is not true. Not a single white victim of the mob was wealthy or had friends or influence to cause a miscarriage of justice. There was no such possibility; it was contempt for law which incited the mob.

from Ida B. Wells, "Lynching and the Excuse for It," *Independent*, May 16, 1901.

Discussion Questions

1. How many lynching victims were there in the last 15 years of the 19th century?
2. What does Wells say actually caused lynching?
3. Why do you think Wells risked her own life to speak out against lynching? Cite evidence from your textbook to support your opinion.

CHAPTER
8

Section 4

LITERATURE SELECTION *from* **Ragtime**
by E. L. Doctorow

In this novel, the lives of three fictional families are entwined with those of such historical figures as industrialist J. P. Morgan, architect Stanford White, social reformer Emma Goldman, and magician Harry Houdini. Read this excerpt to find out what life was like for a typical middle-class white family at the turn of the 20th century.

In 1902 Father built a house at the crest of the Broadview Avenue hill in New Rochelle, New York. It was a three-story brown shingle with dormers, bay windows and a screened porch. Striped awnings shaded the windows. The family took possession of this stout manse on a sunny day in June and it seemed for some years thereafter that all their days would be warm and fair. The best part of Father's income was derived from the manufacture of flags and buntings and other accoutrements of patriotism, including fireworks. Patriotism was a reliable sentiment in the early 1900's. Teddy Roosevelt was President. The population customarily gathered in great numbers either out of doors for parades, public concerts, fish fries, political picnics, social outings, or indoors in meeting halls, vaudeville theatres, operas, ballrooms. There seemed to be no entertainment that did not involve great swarms of people. Trains and steamers and trolleys moved them from one place to another. That was the style, that was the way people lived. Women were stouter then. They visited the fleet carrying white parasols. Everyone wore white in summer. Tennis racquets were hefty and the racquet faces elliptical. There was a lot of fainting. There were no Negroes.There were no immigrants. On Sunday afternoon, after dinner, Father and Mother went upstairs and closed the bedroom door. Grandfather fell asleep on the divan in the parlor. The Little Boy in the sailor blouse sat on the screened porch and waved away the flies. Down at the bottom of the hill Mother's Younger Brother boarded the streetcar and rode to the end of the line. He was a lonely, withdrawn young man with blond moustaches, and was thought to be having difficulty finding himself. The end of the line was an empty field of tall marsh grasses. The air was salt. Mother's Younger Brother in his white linen suit and boater rolled his trousers and walked bare-

Women . . . visited the fleet carrying white parasols. Everyone wore white in summer.

foot in the salt marshes. Sea birds started and flew up. This was the time in our history when Winslow Homer was doing his painting. A certain light was still available along the Eastern seaboard. Homer painted the light. It gave the sea a heavy dull menace and shone coldly on the rocks and shoals of the New England coast. There were unexplained shipwrecks and brave towline rescues. Odd things went on in lighthouses and in shacks nestled in the wild beach plum. Across America sex and death were barely distinguishable. Runaway women died in the rigors of ecstasy. Stories were hushed up and reporters paid off by rich families. One read between the lines of the journals and gazettes. In New York City the papers were full of the shooting of the famous architect Stanford White by Harry K. Thaw, eccentric scion of a coke and railroad fortune. Harry K. Thaw was the husband of Evelyn Nesbit, the celebrated beauty who had once been Stanford White's mistress. The shooting took place in the roof garden of the Madison Square Garden on 26th Street, a spectacular block-long building of yellow brick and terra cotta that White himself had designed in the Sevillian style. It was the opening night of a revue entitled *Mamzelle Champagne,* and as the chorus sang and danced the eccentric scion wearing on this summer night a straw boater and heavy black coat pulled out a pistol and shot the famous architect three times in the head. On the roof. There were screams. Evelyn fainted. She had been a well-known artist's model at the age of fifteen. Her underclothes were white. Her husband habitually whipped her. She happened once to meet Emma Goldman, the revolutionary. Goldman lashed her with her tongue. Apparently there *were* Negroes. There *were* immigrants. And though the papers called the shooting the Crime of the Century, Goldman knew it was only 1906 and there were ninety-four years to go.

Mother's Younger Brother was in love with Evelyn Nesbit. He had closely followed the scandal surrounding her name and had begun to reason that the death of her lover Stanford White and the imprisonment of her husband Harry K. Thaw left her in need of the attentions of a genteel middle-class young man with no money. He thought about her all the time. He was desperate to have her. In his room pinned on the wall was a newspaper drawing by Charles Dana Gibson entitled "The Eternal Question." It showed Evelyn in profile, with a profusion of hair, one thick strand undone and fallen in the configuration of a question mark. Her downcast eye was embellished with a fallen ringlet that threw her brow in shadow. Her nose was delicately upturned. Her mouth was slightly pouted. Her long neck curved like a bird taking wing. Evelyn Nesbit had caused the death of one man and wrecked the life of another and from that he deduced that there was nothing in life worth having, worth wanting, but the embrace of her thin arms.

The afternoon was a blue haze. Tidewater seeped into his footprints. He bent down and found a perfect shell specimen, a variety not common to western Long Island Sound. It was a voluted pink and amber shell the shape of a thimble, and what he did in the hazy sun with the salt drying on his ankles was to throw his head back and drink the minute amount of sea water in the shell. Gulls wheeled overhead, crying like oboes, and behind him at the land end of the marsh, out of sight behind the tall grasses, the distant bell of the North Avenue streetcar tolled its warning.

Across town the little boy in the sailor suit was suddenly restless and began to measure the length of the porch. He trod with his toe upon the runner of the cane-backed rocking chair. He had reached that age of knowledge and wisdom in a child when it is not expected by the adults around him and consequently goes unrecognized. He read the newspaper daily and was currently following the dispute between the professional baseballers and a scientist who claimed that the curve ball was an optical illusion. He felt that the circumstances of his family's life operated against his need to see things and to go places. For instance he had conceived an enormous interest in the works and career of Harry Houdini, the escape artist. But he

had not been taken to a performance. Houdini was a headliner in the top vaudeville circuits. His audiences were poor people—carriers, peddlers, policemen, children. His life was absurd. He went all over the world accepting all kinds of bondage and escaping. He was roped to a chair. He escaped. He was chained to a ladder. He escaped. He was handcuffed, his legs were put in irons, he was tied up in a strait jacket and put in a locked cabinet. He escaped. He escaped from bank vaults, nailed-up barrels, sewn mailbags; he escaped from a zinc-lined Knabe piano case, a giant football, a galvanized iron boiler, a rolltop desk, a sausage skin. His escapes were mystifying because he never damaged or appeared to unlock what he escaped from. The screen was pulled away and there he stood disheveled but triumphant beside the inviolate container that was supposed to have contained him. He waved to the crowd. He escaped from a sealed milk can filled with water. He escaped from a Siberian exile van. From a Chinese torture crucifix. From a Hamburg penitentiary. From an English prison ship. From a Boston jail. He was chained to automobile tires, water wheels, cannon, and he escaped. He dove manacled from a bridge into the Mississippi, the Seine, the Mersey, and came up waving. He hung upside down and strait-jacketed from cranes, biplanes and the tops of buildings. He was dropped into the ocean padlocked in a diving suit fully weighted and not connected to an air supply, and he escaped. He was buried alive in a grave and could not escape, and had to be rescued. Hurriedly, they dug him out. The earth is too heavy, he said gasping. His nails bled. Soil fell from his eyes. He was drained of color and couldn't stand. His assistant threw up. Houdini wheezed and sputtered. He coughed blood. They cleaned him off and took him back to the hotel. Today, nearly fifty years since his death, the audience for escapes is even larger.

The little boy stood at the end of the porch and fixed his gaze on a bluebottle fly traversing the screen in a way that made it appear to be coming up the hill from North Avenue. The fly flew off. An automobile was coming up the hill from North Avenue. As it drew closer he saw it was a black 45-horsepower Pope-Toledo Runabout. He ran along the porch and stood at the top of the steps. The car

> *Houdini was a headliner in the top vaudeville circuits. His audiences were poor people.*

came past his house, made a loud noise and swerved into the telephone pole. The little boy ran inside and called upstairs to his mother and father. Grandfather woke with a start. The boy ran back to the porch. The driver and the passenger were standing in the street looking at the car; it had big wheels with pneumatic tires and wooden spokes painted in black enamel. It had brass headlamps in front of the radiator and brass sidelamps over the fenders. It had tufted upholstery and double side entrances. It did not appear to be damaged. The driver was in livery. He folded back the hood and a geyser of white steam shot up with a hiss.

A number of people looked on from their front yards. But Father, adjusting the chain on his vest, went down to the sidewalk to see if there was something he could do. The car's owner was Harry Houdini, the famous escape artist. He was spending the day driving through Westchester. He was thinking of buying some property. He was invited into the house while the radiator cooled. He surprised them with his modest, almost colorless demeanor. He seemed depressed. His success had brought into vaudeville a host of competitors. Consequently he had to think of more and more dangerous escapes. He was a short, powerfully built man, an athlete obviously, with strong hands and with back and arm muscles that suggested themselves through the cut of his rumpled tweed suit, which, though well tailored, was worn this day inappropriately. The thermometer read in the high eighties. Houdini had unruly stiff hair parted in the middle and clear blue eyes, which did not stop moving. He was very respectful to Mother and Father and spoke of his profession with diffidence. This struck them as appropriate. The little boy stared at him. Mother had ordered lemonade. It was brought into the parlor and Houdini drank it gratefully. The room was kept cool by the awnings on the windows. The windows themselves were shut to keep out the heat. Houdini wanted to undo his collar. He felt trapped by the heavy square furnishings, the drapes and dark rugs, the Oriental silk cushions, the green glass lampshades. There was a chaise with a zebra rug. Noticing Houdini's gaze Father mentioned that he had shot the zebra on a hunting trip in Africa. Father was an amateur explorer of considerable

Houdini then spent a few minutes doing small deft tricks with objects at hand for the little boy.

reputation. He was past president of the New York Explorers Club to which he made an annual disbursement. In fact in just a few days he would be leaving to carry the Club's standard on the third Peary expedition to the Arctic. You mean, Houdini said, you're going with Peary to the Pole? God willing, Father replied. He sat back in his chair and lit a cigar. Houdini became voluble. He paced back and forth. He spoke of his own travels, his tours of Europe. But the Pole! he said. Now that's something. You must be pretty good to get picked for that. He turned his blue eyes on Mother. And keeping the home fires burning ain't so easy either, he said. He was not without charm. He smiled and Mother, a large blond woman, lowered her eyes. Houdini then spent a few minutes doing small deft tricks with objects at hand for the little boy. When he took his leave the entire family saw him to the door. Father and Grandfather shook his hand. Houdini walked down the path that ran under the big maple tree and then descended the stone steps that led to the street. The chauffeur was waiting, the car was parked correctly. Houdini climbed in the seat next to the driver and waved. People stood looking on from their yards. The little boy had followed the magician to the street and now stood at the front of the Pope-Toledo gazing at the distorted macrocephalic image of himself in the shiny brass fitting of the headlight. Houdini thought the boy comely, fair like his mother, and tow-headed, but a little soft-looking. He leaned over the side door. Goodbye, Sonny, he said holding out his hand. Warn the Duke, the little boy said. Then he ran off.

Activity Options

1. Create a chart about life in the early 1900s. Use such headings as Entertainment, Politics, Sports, Race Relations, and Transportation and add details based on your reading of this excerpt.
2. With a small group of classmates, create a collage that captures life at the turn of the century as described in this excerpt and your textbook.
3. Imagine that *Ragtime* is to be distributed as an audio book. With a group of classmates, choose several ragtime compositions that you would use as background music to accompany this excerpt.

AMERICAN LIVES # W. E. B. Du Bois
Scholar, Activist, Critic

*"The world was thinking wrong about race because it did not know. The ulti-
mate evil was stupidity. The cure for it was knowledge based on scientific inves-
tigation."*—W. E. B. Du Bois, Dusk of Dawn (1940)

W. E. B. Du Bois's ideas evolved over his long career. In one thing, however, he was constant. He wanted to highlight the contributions and condition of African Americans because, he once said, "The problem of the twentieth century is the problem of the color line."

Du Bois (1868–1963), born in Massachusetts, received a shock when he reached Fisk University, an all-black college in Nashville, Tennessee. There he experienced for the first time segregation in the South. He later wrote that only an African American "going into the South for the first time can have any conception of [segregation's] barbarism." After graduation from Fisk, he attended Harvard University, where he learned to question accepted ideas.

Du Bois began to teach while he continued work for his Ph.D., which he was awarded in 1895. In his doctoral dissertation, he argued that the slave trade was ended not for moral reasons, but for economic ones. A brilliant study, it made his name as a scholar. Du Bois's next book, *The Philadelphia Negro*, was an equally impressive work of sociology. In it, Du Bois argued forcefully against the idea—quite common at the time—that racial differences were based on genetic traits.

By the turn of the century, Du Bois began a period of political activism. Joining with 28 other African-American intellectuals, he founded the Niagara Movement. This group rejected the views of Booker T. Washington, a leading African American. Washington urged blacks to pursue job training and use economic advances to secure political rights. The Niagara Movement disagreed, flatly stating, "We want full manhood suffrage and we want it now." Du Bois criticized Washington even though Atlanta University, where he worked, depended on financial aid from Washington supporters.

This movement was taken into the National Association for the Advancement of Colored People, formed in 1909. Du Bois left Atlanta University to become editor of the NAACP's journal, *Crisis*. He held the position for 25 years and used it to protest lynching and the denial of rights to African Americans, to celebrate the achievements of African culture, and to promote African-American art. From time to time, he took positions opposed by the NAACP.

One cause of these differences was Du Bois's broadening views and growing socialism. World War I convinced him that the root of African Americans' problems was white imperialism. Slavery and segregation, in this view, were just one aspect of this imperialism, which was also suppressing people of color around the world. Du Bois also began to believe that economic condition determined political status. He urged African Americans to adopt economic segregation from mainstream American life. The NAACP, though, supported integration. Eventually, these differences led him to resign from editing *Crisis*.

Du Bois still had almost three decades of work remaining. In his later writings, he continued to broaden his concern to include the oppressed around the world, especially people of color. He defined Karl Marx's term—the proletariat—as more than just white laborers in Europe and America. This class was "overwhelmingly of the darker workers of Asia, Africa, the islands of the sea, and South Central America . . . who are supporting a superstructure of wealth, luxury, and extravagance." His radical views led to his arrest in the anticommunist hysteria of the 1950s. But Du Bois refused to stop speaking out. In his last major work, a three-novel series called *The Black Flame*, he used fiction to analyze the African-American experience from the end of Reconstruction to the postwar period.

Questions

1. Why was Du Bois startled when he went to Fisk University?
2. What incidents show Du Bois's independence of mind?
3. How did Du Bois's ideas change over time?

CHAPTER

8

Section 4

AMERICAN LIVES **Lillian Gish**

Lifetime Actress, First Lady of Film

"She loves her work and is always ready to tackle the daily responsibilities of whatever role, big or small, she has undertaken. . . . [She] contributed in no small degree to the early development of the art of film making."—Peter Glenville, Preface to Gish's autobiography, The Movies, Mr. Griffith, and Me *(1969)*

Through a lifetime of acting, Lillian Gish (1896–1993) always behaved professionally. One of the first movie stars, she helped establish the film industry by using a natural acting style that moved audiences deeply.

Abandoned by her husband when her daughters were young, Gish's mother struggled. She became an actress and soon put daughters Lillian and Dorothy on stage as well. Acting had a bad reputation, and the Gishes often did not tell other people exactly what it was that they did for a living. Lillian Gish grew up on stage, with hardly any formal schooling. But she developed her mind by reading constantly.

In the course of their performances, the Gishes met a young actress named Gladys Smith. One day they visited Smith—now calling herself Mary Pickford—on the set of a moving picture, an industry that was just beginning. She introduced her friends to director D. W. Griffith, who immediately cast the girls in his film. Unable to tell them apart, he had Lillian wear a blue bow and Dorothy a red one.

For the next decade, the two sisters made many films with Griffith. Lillian's work included some of the pioneering director's most famous works, including the landmark *The Birth of a Nation* (1915). Griffith used Lillian to show his view of the ideal woman—an innocent in a harsh world. She was a sweet farm girl in *True Heart Susie* (1919). In *Broken Blossoms* (1919), she played a victim of abuse who is eventually killed by her father because she had fallen in love with a Chinese immigrant. In *Orphans of the Storm* (1922), Lillian added to this character type. While still an innocent, she shows fierce determination in trying to find her blind sister, played by Dorothy, in the midst of the turmoil of the French Revolution.

Griffith liked Gish because she could display a wide range of emotions. According to some critics, she invented the art of acting on film. She abandoned the broad, sometimes extreme gestures typi-

cal among stage actors. Instead, she used smaller, more subtle movements and facial expressions. The results had a profound impact on audiences. In *The Mothering Heart* (1913), they felt her sorrow and rage when—after her baby died in childbirth—she shredded the petals off a rose. In *Broken Blossoms*, they felt her terror as she hid in a closet from her rampaging father.

Griffith respected Gish's professionalism. In 1920, he asked her to direct Dorothy in *Remodeling Her Husband*. Though the movie succeeded, Gish decided that directing was too much of a burden.

By the time of *Orphans of the Storm*, Gish had grown to be a huge star. Griffith, an independent producer, could not afford to pay her what she could command. He suggested that she sign a rich contract with a studio.

Lillian Gish starred in many films during the 1920s, often suggesting projects to producers. Most notable were her roles in *La Boheme* (1926), *The Scarlet Letter* (1926), and *The Wind* (1928). Then movies became talkies, and audiences began to crave tougher female leads. Gish continued to act, but less frequently in movies. Beginning in 1933, she spent more and more time in the theater, starring in such plays as *Hamlet, Life with Father, The Family Reunion,* and *Uncle Vanya.* She still made occasional movies and, after 1948, appeared from time to time on television. Her last film role was with Bette Davis in the film *The Whales of August.* She was 90 at the time, a complete professional until the end.

Questions

1. Why do you think acting had a bad reputation in the early 1900s?
2. How do you think Gish's childhood shaped her life?
3. What made Gish's acting style different?

Answer Key

Chapter 5, Section 1
GUIDED READING

A. Possible answers:

1. The discovery drew tens of thousands of miners to the west and led to the growth of mining camps and frontier towns.

2. Sand Creek: Five hundred peaceful Cheyenne living on the reservation at Sand Creek, Colorado, were attacked without warning by the U.S. Army; 200 were killed.

3. Treaty of Fort Laramie: The Sioux agreed to live on reservations. Because many Sioux resisted reservation restrictions, and because Sitting Bull never signed it.

4. Little Bighorn: Custer led 200 soldiers against what turned out to be 2,000–3,000 Native American warriors; within twenty minutes, Custer and all his men were killed.

5. Dawes Act: To formalize the policy of assimilation ("Americanization") of Native Americans—by teaching them to want property and to farm.

6. Wounded Knee: The Seventh Cavalry rounded up 340 starving, freezing Sioux and demanded their weapons. After one Sioux warrior fired his rifle, the soldiers used cannons to slaughter 300 of the Native Americans.

B. Answers will vary widely depending upon the specifics noted.

Chapter 5, Section 2
GUIDED READING

A. Possible answers:

1. Land grants: Railroad companies sold frontier land to farmers at low prices; railroad companies recruited Europeans to buy and farm frontier land.

2. Laws passed in 1870s: The Homestead Act offered 160 acres of land free to anyone who would cultivate it for five years; similar acts offered land cheaply or for free in states such as Kansas and Oklahoma.

3. Inventions and improvements: Increased farm productivity by decreasing the amount of effort and time required to produce farm goods

4. Morrill and Hatch Acts: Supported farmers by financing agricultural education and research in farm technology and methodology

B. Hardships: Obtaining enough good land to support a family; bad weather (droughts, floods, blizzards); fires; locust plagues; raids by outlaws; raids by Native Americans; providing food and shelter for themselves; living in dugouts and soddies; needing to be self-sufficient for clothing and medical care; the physical hardships of farm work; financial problems (debt, bankruptcy, fluctuating prices, rising costs of shipping and equipment)

C. Answers will vary widely depending upon the specifics noted.

Chapter 5, Section 3
GUIDED READING

A. Possible answers:

1. Falling crop prices; mortgaged farms and crops; the need to produce more; scarcity of good land; deflation; high transportation and storage costs; the power of railroad companies; secret agreements between railroad companies, grain brokers, and merchants; high rates of interest

2. To bring about inflation and produce "cheap money," so that crop prices would rise and debts would be repaid in dollars that had lost value

3. An increase in the money supply; a graduated income tax; a federal loan program

4. Election of U.S. senators by popular vote; single terms for president and vice-president; the secret ballot to end vote fraud; the eight-hour workday; immigration restrictions

5. City dwellers versus farmers; businessmen and bankers versus farmers and laborers; the industrialized Northeast versus the agrarian South and West; Republicans versus Democrats; gold bugs versus silverites

6. McKinley, a conservative Republican, won with the votes of the urban, industrial East and Middle West; Bryan lost, while carrying the South and the Midwestern farm vote.

B. Answers will vary widely depending upon the specifics noted.

Chapter 5
BUILDING VOCABULARY

A.

1. e	5. b
2. h	6. g
3. f	7. d
4. a	8. c

B.

1. F—Bimetallism is a monetary system based on silver and gold.

2. T

3. F—The Morrill Act gave federal land to the states to help finance agricultural colleges.

4. T

5. F—Sitting Bull, leader of the Hunkpapa Sioux, resisted western settlement by whites.

Chapter 5, Section 1
SKILLBUILDER PRACTICE

Students' work will vary depending upon the topics chosen and specifics noted.

Chapter 5, Section 2
SKILLBUILDER PRACTICE

Models will vary depending on specific details noted.

Chapter 5, Section 1
RETEACHING ACTIVITY

1. b	5. d
2. a	6. c
3. b	7. a
4. c	8. b

Chapter 5, Section 2
RETEACHING ACTIVITY

A.

1. T

2. F—In 1889, settlers claimed some 2 million acres in less than a day in a free land giveaway in what is now Oklahoma.

3. F—Women worked in the fields and on the farms beside men; they also made clothes and other goods for their families as well as ran schools and churches.

4. T

5. F—With forestland scarce on the Plains, most settlers built their homes out of sod.

B.

1. Barbed wire

2. Yellowstone National Park

3. Immigrants

4. John Deere

5. Utah

Chapter 5, Section 3
RETEACHING ACTIVITY

1. falling crop prices; scarcity of good farming land; high prices for equipment; excessive shipping fees charged by railroads

2. teaching its members how to organize, how to set up farmers' cooperatives, and how to sponsor legislation to regulate railroads

3. an increase in the money supply; a graduated income tax and federal loan program; election of U.S. senators by popular vote; single terms for president and vice-president; a secret ballot; an eight-hour workday; restrictions on immigration

4. Thousands of businesses and banks closed and millions of people lost their jobs.

5. The "gold bugs" favored the gold standard, or backing dollars solely with gold; the "silverites" favored bimetallism, or the backing of money with both gold and silver.

6. The populist candidate, William Jennings Bryan, lost to Republican candidate William McKinley.

Chapter 5, Section 2
GEOGRAPHY APPLICATION

Responses may vary on the inferential questions. Sample responses are given for those.

1. mountains

2. the Central Lowlands and the Great Plains

3. Rocky Mountains, Colorado Plateau, Basin and Range Region, Sierra and Cascade Mountains, Great Central Valley, and Pacific Coast Range

4. a. Rocky Mountains; b. Sierra and Cascade Mountains; c. Colorado Plateau; d. Sierra and Cascade Mountains

5. Rocky Mountains

6. 105°W

7. The land bordering the Gulf of Mexico is flat; the land bordering the Pacific Ocean is mountainous.

8. The Wyoming Basin is a lowland area, being a break in the Rocky Mountains. It permitted white settlers a less difficult and quicker route to the West than going over mountainous land.

Chapter 5, Section 1
PRIMARY SOURCE

The Battle of the Little Bighorn

1. Before students begin, have them brainstorm ways to bring the battle to life using descriptive details in Two Moon's account. Suggest that they read other accounts of the Battle of the Little Bighorn in such books as *Bury My Heart at Wounded Knee* by Dee Brown or *Wooden Leg, a Warrior Who Fought Custer* by Thomas B. Marquis. Remind them that their scripts should include ideas for lighting, music, voice-overs, camera angles, and so forth. Then informally assess students' scripts. You may want to have the class work cooperatively to research and prepare a full-length script about the Plains wars, including other battles they have read about.

2. Possible responses:

Causes: the gold rush, the failure of the Treaty of 1868, the policy of the U.S. government toward Native Americans

Effects: the deaths of Custer and all his men, the American public's negative reaction, the exile and surrender of Sitting Bull

3. After students have finished, have them give a brief class presentation in which they present their designs and explain the rationale behind their design choices.

Chapter 5, Section 2
PRIMARY SOURCE

Letter from a Woman Homesteader

1. She proved that a woman could homestead by herself if she wanted to.

2. Some students may say that Stewart's attitude was optimistic and positive. They may point out that her letter refers to the benefits and rewards of hard work and persistence. Others may mention that Stewart viewed homesteading as a challenge that she was determined to meet. A few students may say Stewart's attitude was unrealistic; in her letter, she never addressed the hardships and disappointments of being a homesteader, and she never mentioned the difficulties of getting through the winter.

3. Some students will say that her letter does create a fair portrait because it reflects her firsthand experiences. Others will point out that despite Stewart's positive assessment, women homesteaders generally faced such difficulties as fires, droughts, floods, blizzards, starvation, loneliness, illness, and endless hours of backbreaking work.

Chapter 5, Section 3
PRIMARY SOURCE

The "Cross of Gold" Speech

1. Encourage students to re-create both Bryan's impassioned delivery as well as the exciting atmosphere of a political convention. Tell them that Bryan used a booming voice and broad gestures to capture his audience's attention and that free silverite delegates paraded through the Chicago Amphitheatre wearing silver badges and waving silver banners. Informally assess students' dramatic presentation and their participation in the class discussion that follows.

2. Students' campaign buttons will

vary but should capture the Democratic Party's advocacy of bimetallism or the Republican Party's support of the gold standard. Have students display or wear their buttons.

3. Informally assess students' participation in the mock debate.

Chapter 5, Section 2
LITERATURE SELECTION

My Ántonia

1. Encourage students to include plants and animals mentioned in this passage as well as other species that they find out about. Informally assess the scientific as well as the aesthetic merits of your students' display.

2. Informally assess students' sketches. Encourage them to compare their sketches with Cather's description of the crude dwelling in which the Shimerdas live.

Chapter 5, Section 1
AMERICAN LIVES

Chief Joseph

Possible answers:

1. The war was caused by white settlers' desire for their land and the government's refusal to stand up for the Nez Perce claim to the land. Its immediate cause was the attack by some of Joseph's band on settlers.

2. Joseph's role was primarily political. He represented the Nez Perce in talks with the army and tried to counsel peace.

3. People probably learned that broken promises to Joseph and his ban initiated the struggle. Also, being able to move a large group, including women and children, all while fending off the U.S. Army, probably earned them admiration as underdogs.

Chapter 5, Section 3
AMERICAN LIVES

Mary Elizabeth Lease

Possible answers:

1. Lease used emotional appeals and emotionally charged words.

2. She urged women to enter politics, and she herself attempted to become the first U.S. woman senator.

3. Her book reflected the Populist issues of government control of the railroad and telegraph systems, free silver, and political reforms.

Chapter 6, Section 1
GUIDED READING

Possible answers:

1. Resources: Crude oil; iron ore; coal

2. Drake: Used a steam engine to extract oil from beneath the earth's surface

3. Bessemer process: Was a cheap, efficient method for turning iron ore into steel

4. Steel uses: Railroads; barbed wire; farm machines; bridge and skyscraper construction

5. Edison: Set up a research laboratory; perfected the incandescent light bulb; created a system for producing and distributing electrical power; built power plants

6. Westinghouse: Made electricity safer and less expensive

7. Sholes: Invented the typewriter

8. Bell: Invented the telephone

Chapter 6, Section 2
GUIDED READING

A. Possible answers:

1. Life-threatening working conditions; low pay; discrimination by race or nationality

2. A clean and safe environment, but too controlling, since residents had no say in the town rules and their daily life was strictly controlled

3. Railroad magnates, stockholders in the Union Pacific Railroad, federal officials; to siphon off railroad profits for themselves

4. Sold grant lands to other businesses, instead of to settlers; fixed prices to keep farmers in debt to them; practiced rate discrimination

5. The Supreme Court later reversed the *Munn* decision, ruling that a

state could not set rates on interstate commerce.

6. The ICC's efforts were hampered by long legal processes, the resistance of the railroads, and a Supreme Court ruling that the ICC couldn't set maximum railroad rates.

B. Answers will vary widely depending upon the specifics noted.

Chapter 6, Section 3
GUIDED READING

Possible answers:

1. Vertical integration: a. The process by which a company buys out all of its suppliers; b. Gave a company total power over the quality and cost of its product; helped to create a monopoly

2. Horizontal consolidation: a. The process in which a company buys out, or merges with, its competitors; b. Gave a company control over its competition; helped to create a monopoly

3. Social Darwinism: a. An economic theory based on Darwin's theory of biological evolution; it asserted that free competition would ensure success or failure in business; b. Glorified big business and tycoons; also discouraged government interference with big business

4. Monopoly: a. Complete control over an industry's production, quality, wages, and prices; b. Eliminated a company's competition, allowing it to increase profits

5. Holding company: a. A corporation that does nothing but buy out the stock of other companies; b. Helped to create monopolies

6. Trust: a. A large corporation made up of many companies that receive certificates entitling them to dividends on profits earned by all the companies combined; b. Helped to create monopolies

7. Robber barons: Put tycoons on the defensive; turned public opinion against them and their businesses; finally, encouraged government regulation of big business

8. Sherman Antitrust Act: Made trusts (and monopolies) illegal in interstate and international trade; made

it possible (though not easy) to prosecute companies

Chapter 6
BUILDING VOCABULARY

A.

1. f 5. d
2. g 6. h
3. a 7. c
4. b 8. e

B.

1. Edwin L. Drake
2. Interstate Commerce Act
3. John D. Rockefeller
4. transcontinental railroad
5. Sherman Antitrust Act

C. Answers will vary depending on the specifics noted.

Chapter 6, Section 3
SKILLBUILDER PRACTICE

Students' oral presentations will vary.

Chapter 6, Section 1
RETEACHING ACTIVITY

A.

1. e 4. a
2. f 5. d
3. b 6. c

B.

1. F—The major factors of the nation's industrial boom were a wealth of natural resources, government support for business, and an abundance of farmland.
2. T
3. T
4. F—By 1910, women made up nearly 40 percent of the nation's clerical workforce.
5. F—The rise of the automobile became popular prompted entrepreneurs to transform more oil into gasoline.

Chapter 6, Section 2
RETEACHING ACTIVITY

A.

1. 4 5. 1
2. 5 6. 3
3. 2 7. 8
4. 7 8. 6

B.

1. land grants
2. Chinese; Irish
3. Four
4. Granger laws
5. financial companies

Chapter 6, Section 3
RETEACHING ACTIVITY

1. b 4. c
2. a 5. d
3. b 6. c

Chapter 6, Section 1
GEOGRAPHY APPLICATION

Responses may vary on the inferential questions. Sample responses are given for those.

1. about 11 million
2. 59 percent
3. about 4 million; Although the percentage of farm workers fell, the actual number of such workers increased because the total number of workers increased.
4. the 1880s; percentage of nonfarm workers continued to increase
5. 1860—$150
6. 1860—$360; 1900—$480
7. The U.S. economy suffered from overproduction and overexpansion in both farm and nonfarm areas, causing the earnings of all workers to fall.
8. The number of workers continued to increase substantially while wages stayed virtually the same.

Chapter 6, Section 1
PRIMARY SOURCE

The Birth of the Telephone

1. Students' oral reports may vary. They may mention that the first switchboard began operating in New Haven, Connecticut, in 1878 with 21 subscribers; by 1880 there were 54,000 telephones in service, and by 1900 there were 1.5 million. They may also mention that by 1887 the New York-Philadelphia line was in operation, the first New York-to-Chicago telephone call was made in 1892, and transcontinental service began in 1915. Students may explain that the first telephone operators were men but that by 1900 about 70,000 female operators were employed.
2. You may want to have students post their quotes or sayings on a bulletin board.
3. Informally assess students' biographical sketches about Bell on the basis of accuracy as well as on the quality of their research and writing.

Chapter 6, Section 3
PRIMARY SOURCE

"Wealth and Its Uses"

1. Three uses of wealth: to will it at death to the family, to will it to public institutions, to expend it wisely for the highest good of the people
2. Carnegie endorsed the third use, to spend it for the good of others when one is alive.
3. Most students will likely say that Carnegie did live up to his own philosophy, citing his philanthropy in giving 90 percent of his wealth to worthy causes.

Chapter 6, Section 3
PRIMARY SOURCE

The History of the Standard Oil Company

1. Rockefeller gained control of oil refining and transporting and then set out to control the oil markets of the world.
2. Some students might say that Rockefeller deserved to be called a

robber baron since he used ruthless tactics to build a monopoly and earn a great deal of money. Others may say that Rockefeller did not deserve such an epithet because he used keen business skills to become wealthy.

Chapter 6, Section 3
PRIMARY SOURCE

Labor Poster

1. Some students may say that the poster conveys strength, power, productivity, and unity. Other students may say that the poster sends a message of intimidation, aggression, violence, and force.

2. Some students may indicate that the bold graphic images of a young, strong worker and factory smokestacks are most persuasive because they depict the vitality and productivity of industry. Others may say that the simple, powerful slogans are most persuasive because they capture the hope and promise of joining a labor union.

3. Possible responses: because they encouraged people to think about the IWW and persuaded workers to join the union.

Chapter 6, Section 2
LITERATURE SELECTION

"The Bride Comes to Yellow Sky"

1. Before students begin, encourage them to describe their own first-hand experiences of train travel. Then informally assess students' discussion.

2. Informally assess students' sketches. Encourage them to draw either the dining car or the coach car in which the newlyweds ride to Yellow Sky.

3. Students' postcards will vary but should include realistic details about why the newlyweds took the trip, what the train car looked like, how long the trip to Yellow Sky took, what scenery could be observed from the train, how the other passengers reacted, what the meal in the dining car was like, and so on.

Chapter 6, Section 3
AMERICAN LIVES

Andrew Carnegie

Possible answers:

1. Carnegie did something "exceptional" in learning to read telegraph messages when only a messenger, and his organization of rail and telegraph systems in the Civil War showed his abilities "beyond the range of his special department."

2. Carnegie's "gospel of wealth" is an admirable idea, although calling it a "duty" to help others may be putting it too strongly.

3. His money given to colleges and his creation of about 3,000 public libraries are probably his lasting contribution.

Chapter 6, Section 3
AMERICAN LIVES

Mary Harris "Mother" Jones

Possible answers:

1. Jones's appearance probably helped her. Officials who might have been willing to use force on a male union organizer would have been less willing to use force on an older woman.

2. By getting publicity, Jones could win wider public support for the union cause.

3. Management feared Jones because she was good at rousing workers to action when management took advantage of them. Law-enforcement officials feared her because union organizing drives sometimes went beyond action to violence.

Chapter 7, Section 1
GUIDED READING

A. Possible answers:

1. Countries: Italy, Austria-Hungary, Russia

   Reasons: to escape religious persecution; to escape problems caused by overpopulation; to find good farmland and jobs; to lead freer, more independent lives

   Where: Ellis Island

2. Countries: China, Japan

   Reasons: to make money; to seek their fortunes; to mine gold; to obtain better paying jobs

   Where: Angel Island

3. Countries: Mexico, Jamaica, Cuba, Puerto Rico, other islands in the West Indies

   Reasons: to find work; lived in territories taken over by the U.S.; to flee political turmoil

   Where: Ellis Island; southeastern U.S.; southwestern U.S.

B. Possible answers:

Native-born Americans spoke English; new immigrants often did not.

Native-born Americans tended to have ancestors from western Europe; new immigrants came from other parts of the world.

Native-born Americans tended to be Caucasian; many of the new immigrants were Asian.

Native-born Americans tended to be Protestant; many new immigrants were Catholics or Jews.

C. Answers will vary widely depending upon the specifics noted.

Chapter 7, Section 2
GUIDED READING

A. Possible answers:

1. Immigrants: Cities cheaper and more convenient; ethnic neighborhoods and cultural opportunities not found in rural areas

2. Farmers: Fewer farm laborers needed because of new technology; believed jobs could be found in cities; cultural opportunities not found in rural areas

3. African Americans: Fewer farm laborers needed because of new technology; believed jobs could be found in cities; hope of less racial violence and political oppression than in the South; cultural opportunities not found in rural areas

4. Transportation: Construction of mass-transit networks, based on such new forms of transportation as cable cars, electric streetcars, and electric subways

5. Water: Chlorination and filtration

6. Sanitation: Sewer lines and sanitation departments

7. Fire hazards: Full-time professional fire departments and the automatic fire sprinkler; replacement of many wooden buildings with structures made of brick, stone, and concrete

8. Crime: Full-time professional police departments

B. Answers will vary widely depending upon the specifics noted.

Chapter 7, Section 3
GUIDED READING

A. Possible answers:

1. Supported reform; named independents to his cabinet; set up a commission to investigate customshouses; fired two top officials of the New York customshouse

2. The reformers

3. Supported reform; urged Congress to pass a civil service law (the Pendleton Act)

4. Authorized a bipartisan civil service commission to make appointments based on the merit system

5. Supported a low tariff; tried to convince Congress to lower rates; ran for a second term on a low-tariff platform

6. Supported a high tariff; won passage of the McKinley Tariff Act, which raised tariffs to their highest level ever

7. They were lowered.

8. They were raised.

B. Answers will vary widely depending upon the specifics noted.

Chapter 7
BUILDING VOCABULARY

A.

1. F—As part of the Gentleman's Agreement, Japan's government agreed to limit immigration of unskilled workers to the United States.

2. T

3. F—Tenements, multifamily urban

dwellings, were often overcrowded and unsanitary.

4. T

5. T

B.

1. Rutherford B. Hayes

2. Social Gospel Movement

3. Ellis Island

4. melting pot

5. nativism

C. Answers will vary depending on the specifics noted.

Chapter 7, Section 1
SKILLBUILDER PRACTICE

Maps will vary, but should convey all information accurately and clearly.

Chapter 7, Section 3
SKILLBUILDER PRACTICE

1. A corrupt politician

2. The city treasury; by using falsified accounts

3. Through his corrupt tactics, the politician was able to cut through the red tape of government.

4. That it was easy for corrupt politicians to cheat the taxpayers.

Chapter 7, Section 1
RETEACHING ACTIVITY

A.

1. Jews

2. Chinese

3. literacy test

4. Religious

5. steamship

B.

Chinese Exclusion Act—banned entry to all Chinese except students, teachers, merchants, tourists, and government officials

Gentlemen's Agreement—limited immigration of unskilled Japanese workers to the United States in exchange for the repeal of the San

Francisco order segregating Japanese school children

Chapter 7, Section 2
RETEACHING ACTIVITY

1. b	4. a
2. b	5. a
3. c	6. d

Chapter 7, Section 3
RETEACHING ACTIVITY

A.

1. 2	4. 1
2. 4	5. 6
3. 5	6. 3

B.

1. Grover Cleveland

2. Thomas Nast

3. immigrants

4. kickbacks

5. business

Chapter 7, Section 2
GEOGRAPHY APPLICATION

Responses may vary on the inferential questions. Sample responses are given for those.

1. 1879—textiles; 1909—food and drink

2. cotton goods; leather products

3. The tenth-ranked industry in 1909 (printing and publishing) was worth more than the top-ranked industry of 1879 (textiles) had been worth; about 6 times greater

4. Consumer products and other items were being increasingly made out of longer-lasting, more durable materials.

5. In 1879, the iron and steel industry was worth only a little more than half of the top-ranked industry. But 30 years later, iron and steel had a worth of about five-sixths of the top-ranked industry.

6. 1880—12.3 percent; 1910—22 percent

7. It rose from 42.9 percent to 76.9 percent.

8. The three cities that already had more than 1,000,000 people were continuing to add even more people at a high rate during that period.

Chapter 7, Section 2
OUTLINE MAP

1. east

2. fewer than two people per square mile

3. Illinois, Indiana, Ohio, and Pennsylvania

4. Wisconsin, Michigan, Florida, New York, and Maine; Iowa, Missouri, and Arkansas

5. an area of population density of more than 90 people per square mile

6. Possible answer: All four categories of population density were found in Minnesota. The area of density of more than 90 people per square mile was found around Minneapolis. The other three categories comprised nearly equal amounts of land—about one-third of the state.

7. The Los Angeles area has gone from having a low population-density category to having a very high one.

Chapter 7, Section 1
PRIMARY SOURCE

Artifacts from Ellis Island

1. Students' lists will vary but should include questions about why the immigrant left his or her homeland, what the journey was like, what the immigration process entailed, and how the immigrant felt when glimpsing America for the first time.

2. Informally assess students' selection of a guest speaker and their discussion afterwards. If they choose someone who lives or works in your community, assist them in writing or calling to invite this person to your class.

3. Informally assess students' poems. Encourage them to read their poems aloud to the class. You may want to have students work collaboratively to put together a booklet of immigration poems.

Chapter 7, Section 2
PRIMARY SOURCE

How the Other Half Lives

1. Possible responses: housing, water, sanitation, and fire

2. Students will likely say that children were frequently the victims of serious illness and violence. They may also mention that children were forced to endure hunger, boredom, and unsanitary, depressing living conditions.

3. Possible responses:

   Sights: dark, dingy halls; soiled white bow on a door; loaded down fire escapes; patched rags hanging on a clothesline

   Sounds: slamming hall door; squeaking pump; baby's hacking cough and tiny wail; quarrelling, coarse songs, and profanity heard behind closed doors

   Smells: summer stenches, smell of the saloon, smell of soapsuds and boiling cabbage

Chapter 7, Section 2
PRIMARY SOURCE

Twenty Years at Hull-House

1. Informally assess students' oral reports. You may want to encourage them to focus in-depth on one particular settlement house in the United States or on one settlement-house worker.

2. Informally assess the clarity and accuracy of students' author's notes. You may want to encourage them to design and display a book jacket on which their author's notes might appear.

Chapter 7, Section 3
PRIMARY SOURCE

The Shame of the Cities

Possible responses:

1. Philadelphia's political machine made sure its candidates would win by padding voting lists, controlling the election officers, and using police intimidation.

2. Philadelphians literally did not vote because they were intimidated by the political machine. In addition, even those who did go to the polls in essence did not vote because the machine—not honest citizens who voted freely—determined the outcome of elections.

3. Some students may say that Philadelphia's political machine flourished because it used election fraud. Others may say it flourished because honest citizens and the police did not actively fight against it. A few students may believe that other factors at the time, such as rapid urbanization, inefficient government, and a climate of Social Darwinism helped the machine flourish.

Chapter 7, Section 1
LITERATURE SELECTION

Call It Sleep

1. Before students begin, have them use Roth's descriptive details to help them visualize their subjects. Then informally assess students' sketches. As an alternative to this activity, you may want to have the class work together to create a collage consisting of images related to immigration in general and to this excerpt in particular.

2. Informally assess students' role-play and their discussion about the Schearls.

3. Before students begin, provide them with blank index cards. Have them illustrate one side of the card and write their postcard message on the other. Then informally assess students' work.

Chapter 7, Section 2
AMERICAN LIVES

Jane Addams

Possible answers:

1. The language and job skills programs were probably the most beneficial, as they gave the immigrants practical skills.

2. In Addams's time, middle-class women were cultivated to the point where they lacked real-life experiences. Frustration over these limita-

tions explains why Addams wanted to start the settlement house.

3. Programs like Addams's settlement house, uniting the poor and the better-off in common tasks, would benefit society today.

Chapter 7, Section 3
AMERICAN LIVES

William Marcy "Boss" Tweed

Possible answers:

1. Democrat Tweed got a friend to run as an independent Whig candidate against him, thereby splitting the opposition Whig vote and allowing Tweed to win.

2. Tweed "owned" elected officials by virtue of his running and winning their campaigns for them. This purchased loyalty protected him as he defrauded the city government.

3. Accounting records would show how much money the government was taking in and possibly reveal where that money was going.

Chapter 8, Section 1
GUIDED READING

A. Possible answers:

1. Skyscraper: Louis Sullivan; Daniel Burnham

   Electric transit: (blank)

   Suspension bridge: John Augustus Roebling

   Urban planning: Frederick Law Olmsted; Calvert Vaux; Daniel Burnham

   Airmail: Orville and Wilbur Wright

   Web-perfecting press: (blank)

   Kodak camera: George Eastman

2. Skyscraper: the elevator; internal steel skeletons

   Electric transit: electricity

   Suspension bridge: steel cables

   Urban planning: (blank)

   Airmail: the airplane; the internal combustion engine

   Web-perfecting press: cheap, durable paper; electricity

   Kodak camera: the camera, new film-processing techniques

3. Skyscraper: Used limited and expensive urban space more efficiently

   Electric transit: Allowed city workers to live in suburbs; spurred the growth of suburbs; reduced congestion on city streets

   Suspension bridge: Tied sections of cities together; sometimes provided recreational opportunities

   Urban planning: Promoted a greater sense of serenity and well-being by creating open spaces in cities

   Airmail: Sped the delivery of mail

   Web-perfecting process: Made printed materials more affordable; satisfied Americans' increasing demand for books, magazines, and newspapers

   Kodak camera: Brought photography within the reach of the average American

B. Answers will vary widely depending upon the specifics noted.

Chapter 8, Section 2
GUIDED READING

A. Possible answers:

1. Strict discipline; a push for compulsory school attendance; a curriculum emphasis on reading, writing, and arithmetic; an emphasis on rote memorization; physical punishment; a surge in kindergartens; an overall pattern of growth; few public schools open to African-American children; the growth of parochial schools

2. An overall pattern of growth; the curriculum expanded to cover science, civics, home economics, history, literature, and vocational training; few public schools open to African-American children; African-American students attended private high schools.

3. An overall pattern of growth; most students middle- or upper-class; research universities offered courses in modern languages, engineering, economics, physical sciences, psychology, and sociology, as well as professional courses in law and medicine; African-American universities and institutes founded.

4. Night schools taught immigrants

citizenship skills and English; employers offered daytime courses to "Americanize" their workers.

B. Answers will vary widely depending upon the specifics noted.

Chapter 8, Section 3
GUIDED READING

A. Possible answers:

1. Region: South

   Who: African Americans, illiterate whites

   How: Prevented them from voting; weakened their political power

2. Region: South

   Who: Poor African Americans, poor whites

   How: Prevented them from voting; weakened their political power

3. Region: South

   Who: African Americans

   How: Prevented them from voting; weakened their political power

4. Region: South

   Who: African Americans

   How: Segregated them into facilities separate from those of whites; forced them to endure second-class services from schools, hospitals, parks, transportation services, and so on

5. Region: All, but especially in the South

   Who: African Americans

   How: Belittled and humiliated them on a daily basis; made interaction with whites extremely dangerous; forced them to show deference to whites; made most forms of success dangerous

6. Region: West; Southwest

   Who: Mexican Americans, African Americans

   How: Forced them to work against their will to pay a debt; made them little more than slaves; denied them the ability to live their own lives

7. Region: All

   Who: Chinese, Chinese Americans

   How: Prohibited Chinese immigration to the U.S.; suspended naturalization for Chinese who were already present

B. Answers will vary widely depending upon the specifics noted.

Chapter 8, Section 4
GUIDED READING

A. Possible answers:

1. Amusement parks example: Coney Island

   Reason: escape

2. Bicycling example: Safety bicycle

   Reason: Freed women from chaperones

3. Boxing example: John L. Sullivan, James J. "Gentleman Jim" Corbett

   Reason: Offered an escape from work and everyday concerns

4. Baseball example: National League, Negro American League

   Reason: Offered an escape from work

5. Shopping centers example: in Cleveland, Ohio

   Reason: Large quantities of reasonably priced manufactured goods

6. Department stores example: Marshall Field

   Reason: Offered personalized services

7. Chain stores example: F. W. Woolworth

   Reason: Offered bargain prices

8. Mail-order catalogs example: Montgomery Ward, Sears and Roebuck

   Reason: Brought department-store merchandise to farmers and residents of small towns

B. Answers will vary widely depending upon the specifics noted.

Chapter 8
BUILDING VOCABULARY

A.

1. e
2. g
3. h
4. f
5. b
6. d
7. c
8. a

B.

1. Booker T. Washington
2. Niagra Movement
3. poll tax
4. William Randolph Hearst
5. rural free delivery

C. Answers will vary depending on the specifics noted.

Chapter 8, Section 3
SKILLBUILDER PRACTICE

Answers will vary. Sample response: a photograph of white and colored drinking fountains or restrooms to show the widespread segregation in the Jim Crow South; a map of the segregated neighborhoods of a Northern city to show that discrimination and prejudice against African Americans existed in the North as well as in the South; a Web site about the history of Mexican-Americans, with a focus on the page that addresses the discrimination they faced in the early twentieth century; an enlarged copy of the Chinese ExclusionAct to demonstrate the fear and anger many Americans felt toward the immigration of the Chinese.

Chapter 8, Section 1
RETEACHING ACTIVITY

A.

1. F—By the turn of the twentieth century about four out of ten Americans made their homes in cities.
2. T
3. F—The first successful flight took place in Kitty Hawk, North Carolina.
4. F—The "Emerald Necklace" refers to the city of Boston's park system.
5. T

B.

1. architecture
2. urban planning
3. urban planning
4. flight
5. photography

Chapter 8, Section 2
RETEACHING ACTIVITY

1. The increasingly industrial economy demanded advanced technical and managerial skills.
2. To become more "Americanized" by learning the English language and American customs.
3. They expanded their curricula to included courses in science, civics, and social studies, as well as vocational courses that prepared male graduates for industrial jobs and female graduates for office work.
4. They emphasized courses in modern languages, the physical sciences, and the new disciplines of psychology and sociology.
5. They opened their own universities with the help of the Freedmen's Bureau and financial donors.
6. Washington stressed acquiring labor skills and providing economic value to society, while Du Bois advocated a liberal-arts education to provide well-educated leaders.

Chapter 8, Section 3
RETEACHING ACTIVITY

A.

Poll tax—required voters to pay a tax, which many African Americans could not afford and thus they could not vote.

Jim Crow laws—laws that separated black and white people in public and private facilities

Plessy v. Ferguson—Supreme Court decisions that established the doctrine of "separate but equal," which allowed states to maintain separate facilities for whites and blacks

B.

1. racial discrimination
2. Mexicans
3. Thirteenth Amendment
4. grandfather clause

Chapter 8, Section 4
RETEACHING ACTIVITY

1. b
4. b

2. b   5. c
3. d   6. a

Chapter 8, Section 1
GEOGRAPHY APPLICATION

Responses may vary on the inferential questions. Sample responses are given for those.

1. to produce a poetic influence in people's minds through scenic beauty; to make life in a city happier and healthier

2. He pioneered the use of natural landscaping in the development of urban parks.

3. Trees and shrubs were planted all around the park to shut out the city, traffic was routed underground, artificial lakes were created, and bridle paths and footpaths were laced throughout the park.

4. museums and a planetarium, statues, and zoos; places for rowing, walking, and appreciating nature

5. It is two-and-a-half miles long and one-half mile wide.

6. northeast

7. the idea that making natural areas available for use by urban residents is important to the quality of life in large cities

8. Answers will vary.

Chapter 8, Section 1
PRIMARY SOURCE

Orville Wright's Diary

1. 4

2. On the fourth and last trip, Wilbur Wright flew 852 feet in 59 seconds.

3. They had difficulty keeping the plane steady and encountered windy conditions and equipment problems, such as a broken flight lever and a damaged front rudder frame.

Chapter 8, Section 1
PRIMARY SOURCE

Advertisement

1. Informally assess students' Venn diagrams.

2. Letters will vary. Students should include advantages—simple to use, convenient to carry, easy to hold—as well as disadvantages, such as having to send the camera to the Eastman Dry Plate and Film Company in Rochester, New York, for reloading before using it again.

3. Informally assess students' ads on the basis of creativity and historical accuracy. Invite students to display their ads in the classroom.

Chapter 8, Section 2
PRIMARY SOURCE

"The Talented Tenth"

1. Invite students to present their introductions and then informally assess their work on the basis of coherency, clarity, and accuracy.

2. Suggest that students use the *Statistical Abstract of the United States* or similar resources to find current statistics. You may want to encourage students to create a bar graph to present their findings.

Chapter 8, Section 3
PRIMARY SOURCE

"Lynching and the Excuse for It"

1. According to Wells, 2,000 men, women, and children were lynched from 1885 to 1900.

2. Wells said lynching was caused by a contempt for law and by race prejudice.

3. Some students may believe that Wells risked her life because as an African-American woman she felt a moral duty to fight against discrimination and violence. Others may cite her personal experience in losing three friends to lynching as her motivation. A few may say that as a journalist Wells was driven to pursue the facts and to reveal the truth.

Chapter 8, Section 4
LITERATURE SELECTION

Ragtime

1. Possible responses:

Entertainment: Harry Houdini, parades, public concerts, vaudeville,

celebrities, scandals, crime

Politics: Emma Goldman, President Teddy Roosevelt

Sports: tennis, baseball

Race Relations: discrimination against African Americans and immigrants

Transportation: steamers, trolleys, trains, 45-horsepower car

2. Informally assess students' participation in creating the collage. Encourage them to add a title and then display their collage.

3. Informally assess students' selection of music. You may want to encourage them to tape-record a reading of this passage with the background music they chose.

Chapter 8, Section 2
AMERICAN LIVES

W. E. B. Du Bois

Possible answers:

1. Growing up in Massachusetts, he had not previously experienced segregation.

2. Du Bois criticized Booker T. Washington even though his university depended on the support of Washington backers, and he urged economic segregation even though the NAACP backed integration.

3. As time went on, Du Bois saw the problems of African Americans in a broader—and more economic—context as part of the suffering caused by white imperialism.

Chapter 8, Section 4
AMERICAN LIVES

Lillian Gish

Possible answers:

1. Actors did not engage in "respectable" work and were thought to have loose morals.

2. If it hadn't been for her family's financial troubles, Gish probably would not have entered acting.

3. Gish's style was more subtle; other actors of the day used broader gestures and facial expressions.

CURRICULUM